THE CONSTRUCTION OF BUILDINGS

VOLUME 5

Supply and Discharge Services

WATER SUPPLY, SANITARY APPLIANCES,

SANITARY PIPEWORK, FOUL DRAINAGE,

ROOF AND SURFACE WATER DRAINAGE,

ELECTRICAL SUPPLY, GAS SUPPLY,

REFUSE STORAGE

R. BARRY
Architect

SECOND EDITION

OXFORD

BLACKWELL SCIENTIFIC PUBLICATIONS

LONDON EDINBURGH BOSTON

MELBOURNE PARIS BERLIN VIENNA

© R. Barry 1978, 1988

Blackwell Scientific Publications
Editorial Offices:
Osney Mead, Oxford OX2 0EL
25 John Street, London WC1N 2BL
23 Ainslie Place, Edinburgh EH3 6AJ
3 Cambridge Center, Cambridge,
  Massachusetts 02142, USA
54 University Street, Carlton,
  Victoria 3053, Australia

Other Editorial Offices:
Librairie Arnette SA
2, rue Casimir-Delavigne
75006 Paris
France

Blackwell Wissenschafts-Verlag
Meinekestrasse 4
D-1000 Berlin 15
Germany

Blackwell MZV
Feldgasse 13
A-1238 Wien
Austria

First Edition published in Great Britain by
  Crosby Lockwood Staples Ltd 1978
Reprinted 1979
Reprinted by Granada Publishing 1980
Reprinted by Collins Professional and Technical Books 1985
Second Edition published by BSP Professional Books 1988
Reprinted 1989, 1990
Reprinted by Blackwell Scientific Publications 1992

Set by DP Photosetting, Aylesbury, Bucks
Printed and bound in Great Britain by
Billing & Sons Ltd, Worcester

DISTRIBUTORS

Marston Book Services Ltd
PO Box 87
Oxford OX2 0DT
(*Orders:* Tel: 0865 791155
          Fax: 0865 791927
          Telex: 837515)

USA
Blackwell Scientific Publications, Inc.
3 Cambridge Center
Cambridge, MA 02142
(*Orders:* Tel: 800 759-6102
             617 225-0401)

Canada
Oxford University Press
70 Wynford Drive
Don Mills
Ontario M3C 1J9
(*Orders:* Tel: 416 441-2941)

Australia
Blackwell Scientific Publications
(Australia) Pty Ltd
54 University Street
Carlton, Victoria 3053
(*Orders:* Tel: 03 347-0300)

British Library
Cataloguing in Publication Data

A catalogue record for this book is
available from the British Library

ISBN 0-632-02248-5

CONTENTS

INTRODUCTION

This revision of Volume 5 includes changes in the regulations for the supply of water and to sanitary pipework and foul drains.

Since the Waterwork Clauses Act of 1847, regulations governing the supply of water to buildings have changed little. In Britain it has been a general requirement of byelaws controlling the supply of water that each building has a cold water storage cistern from which cold water supplies are drawn, whereas in most European countries the use of a cold water storage cistern has long since been abandoned as 'expensive, unhygienic and unnecessary'. The Model Water Byelaws 1986 will be the basis of new byelaws to be made by water authorities in Great Britain sometime in 1988. These new byelaws will give all building owners the option of using the long-established cold water storage cistern, gravity feed for all cold supplies, other than one mains drinking outlet, or to take all cold water supplies direct from the mains and dispense with a cold water storage cistern.

This, for Great Britain, radical departure from antiquated systems has not been publicised and is very cautiously hinted at in the new byelaws.

A consequence of the option to change to a mains pressure cold water supply is that unvented mains pressure supplied hot water storage systems can be used to provide a more vigorous flow of hot water than is generally possible with gravity feed supplies from a cold water storage cistern.

The changes in regard to sanitary appliances are the permitted use of a mascerator (shredder) and pump to small bore discharge pipes from WCs so that they may be some distance from discharge stacks or fixed in basements.

The Approved Documents published with the Building Regulations 1985 give practical guidance to meeting the requirements of the Regulations. Approved Document H1 gives practical guidance on sanitary pipework and drainage. This Approved Document includes guidance on sanitary pipework and foul drains, that follows on from the earlier work by the Building Research Station included in their publication in 1952. There are some modifications of detail in the use of the single stack system of pipework for economy in pipe runs and the inclusion of the permitted use of air admittance valves to internal ventilation stacks.

The Approved Document H1 accepts the granular bed and flexible joints to foul drains as being the method of bedding and jointing for drain runs generally, and finally disposes of the ridiculous and vastly expensive notion of cast iron drains on and surrounded by concrete that has been a requirement in many local authority districts, particularly in urban areas of this country.

ACKNOWLEDGEMENTS

Extracts from British standards are reproduced by permission of BSI. Complete copies of the standards can be obtained from them at Linford Wood, Milton Keynes, Bucks MK14 6LE.

Extracts from the Water Supply Byelaws Guide are reproduced with permission from the Water Research Centre.

Tables 5, 6, 8, 9, 10, 11, 12, and 13 are reproduced from Approved Document H of The Building Regulations with the permission of the Controller of Her Majesty's Stationery Office.

CHAPTER ONE

WATER SUPPLY

WATER SUPPLY

Quantity: There is no overall shortage of water in this country. In an average year rainfall over England and Wales is 900 mm half of which is lost by evaporation and transpiration, leaving an average of 190 million cubic metres per day from which the public water supplies and industry take about 18 million cubic metres. Thus the direct supply consumption, including industry and agriculture is about 10% of the potential supply available from rainwater.

The organisation of public water supply is therefore, obviously concerned not with the quantity of water available but with collection and storage in order to cover seasonal variations and requirements, the movement of water from areas of surplus to areas of shortage and the overall control and treatment of effluents to avoid pollution and maintain the quality of water supplies.

Sources of water: In low-lying areas water is mainly drawn from rivers and stored in reservoirs to provide against seasonal variations in supply and demand and in which the chemical and biological content of the water may be controlled. In upland areas, water

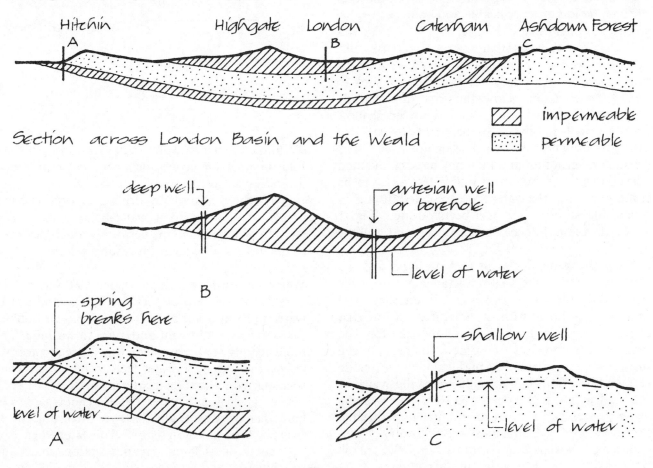

Fig. 1

1

is usually stored in natural or man-made lakes fed by run-off from the surrounding higher ground and in reservoirs fed by wells and boreholes. Most urban and rural areas of this country are served by a supply of water piped from the water suppliers' main. The water authorities are required by statute to provide a supply of wholesome water for which they may require a capital contribution towards the cost of running the supply pipes from their nearest main to new buildings. In outlying areas it may be more economical to draw supply from a well or borehole than pay the capital contribution.

Wells, boreholes and springs: A well is a shaft sunk or excavated below the level of ground water or into sub-soil water bearing strata. The shaft, usually circular, is lined with brick, stone or pre-cast concrete sections to maintain the sides of the well. A borehole is a steel-lined shaft driven or drilled into the ground to a water-bearing stratum. Springs break where the water level in a permeable stratum is above the level of the junction of a permeable and an impermeable stratum as illustrated in Fig. 1.

Wells are defined as shallow wells and deep wells. A shallow well is one that is sunk to collect surface or ground water, and a deep well is one that is sunk to collect water from below the first impermeable stratum. The distinction is made between shallow and deep wells in relation to the quality or purity of the water drawn from each. The shallow well draws surface and ground water that may be contaminated whereas water from a deep well is less likely to be contaminated as the water has percolated through a permeable stratum and has been purified. Fig. 1 illustrates the difference between deep and shallow wells.

Wells are generally excavated by hand and the least diameter of the well is dictated by the space required for the excavator to work in the shaft. The well hole is lined with stone, brick or pre-cast concrete rings. The lining of a shallow well should be rendered impermeable for some distance from the surface with a surround of puddled clay to exclude surface water that may be polluted, as illustrated in Fig. 2. The lining of a deep well should likewise be made impermeable down to the first impermeable stratum to exclude surface and ground water. Water is raised from wells by a pump (see Fig. 2). Shallow wells may dry up during the summer months.

An artesian well is sunk, in a valley, to a permeable

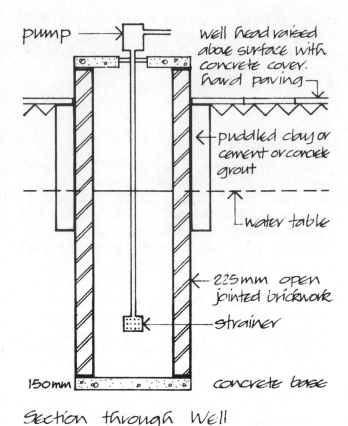

Section through Well

Fig. 2

stratum from which water rises with force from the folded permeable layer sandwiched between impermeable layers as illustrated in Fig. 1.

A borehole is sunk by driving or drilling steel-lining tubes down to a water-bearing permeable stratum. Water enters the perforated or slotted shoe of the tubes and is raised by a force pump.

Water for washing – hard water, soft water: The constituents of soap disperse oil, grease and dirt in water to form a lather or foam of minute bubbles that serve as a lubricant and assist in washing. The more readily soap combines with water to form a lather, the softer the water feels to the touch when washing. Water that readily forms a lather with soap is said to be soft and water that does not is said to be hard. The words soft and hard are used subjectively to express the common sense feel of water when used with soap for washing. The descriptions, hard and soft, have been adopted to define the mineral content of water.

Temporary hardness – permanent hardness: Much of the water drawn from underground sources such as chalk and limestone beds and from surface water in clay deposits, is said to be hard. Free carbon dioxide in underground water combines with chalk or limestone to form calcium bicarbonate, which is soluble in water (temporary hardness) and calcium and magnesium sulphate and chloride (permanent hardness).

When soap is dissolved in hard water it reacts with the minerals in the water to form a scum on the surface before it combines with water to form a lather. The excessive rubbing required to form a lather together with the scum formed is the reason the water is described as hard. More soap is required to form a lather in hard water than in soft water. It is advantageous, therefore, to treat hard water to reduce the hardness for washing purposes.

The following is a table of the degree of hardness of water. Hardness is measured in mg/l as $CaCo_3$.

0—50	mg/l	soft
50—100	mg/l	moderately soft
100—150	mg/l	slightly soft
150—200	mg/l	moderately hard
over 200	mg/l	hard
over 300	mg/l	very hard

The range of hardness acceptable for general washing purposes lies between 100 and 200 mg/l.

Water as a vehicle for heat transfer: When water is boiled the soluble mineral bicarbonates form a hard scale inside kettles, pans and inside hot-water and heating boilers and pipes. The scale is a poor conductor of heat and as it builds up inside kettles and boilers, progressively more fuel is required to heat the water, thus wasting energy. In time, heating and hot-water pipes may become blocked by the build up of scale. The harder the water and the higher the temperature the greater the build up of scale. There is, therefore, economic advantage in controlling the hardness of water.

Because the mineral bicarbonate hardness of water is converted to scale by heating, it is described as 'temporary hardness' or more accurately 'carbonate hardness'. The non-carbonate mineral content of water, that is unaffected by heating, is termed 'permanent hardness' or 'non-carbonate hardness'. Bicarbonates of calcium and magnesium dissolved in water cause temporary hardness and sulphates and chlorides, permanent hardness.

Drinking water: For drinking, many prefer the taste or palatability of soft water from deep wells and fast-flowing streams, while others prefer the taste of a hard water. The temperature of the water affects the subjective judgement of taste, the colder the water the more palatable it is said to be. Most will agree that stagnant water and especially tepid stagnant water has an unpleasant taste. Obviously there is no generally accepted measure of taste.

Water quality – acidity, alkalinity: Rain water and water that contains decomposing organic matter such as peat, is acid water. Acid water is corrosive to iron and steel and will take lead into solution. As acid water is plumbo-solvent, lead pipes should not be used in distributing acid water as lead is a cumulative poison.

Alkaline water contains calcium bicarbonate which is the constituent of temporary hardness.

Pure water consists of hydrogen and oxygen and a small number of positive and negative ions. The measure of the acidity or alkalinity of water is pH, the letters used to denote the concentration of hydrogen ions. An acid water has a pH value of less than 7.0 and alkaline water above 7.0.

Water quality – purity, wholesomeness: The measure of the purity or wholesomeness of water is its freedom from pathogens which may be the cause of waterborne diseases in man. The waterborne diseases are generally caused by the pollution of water by untreated or partly treated sewage.

It is not practicable to test water for traces of pathogens. Instead samples are taken for evidence of pollution by sewage as an indication of the likelihood of disease-carrying pathogens.

Water is purified by sedimentation and filtration and by the addition of very small doses of chlorine to the water. The action of chlorine in water is disinfection whereby the chlorine reduces the infectious organisms to extremely low levels.

Water treatment – water purification: Water is usually treated to change a hard water to a soft or a softer water to reduce scale formation and facilitate washing. Two methods are used: in the first lime, or lime with soda are added to the water, which brings

3

about changes to the hardness compounds so that they become insoluble and precipitate by settlement or in filters, and in the second the nature of the hardness is changed in a base exchange softener. In the first method the hardness compounds are changed and removed, and in the second the hardness compounds are changed and remain in the water. In the second method of softening a natural or synthetic zeolite is used to convert compounds of calcium and magnesium to sodium carbonate-bicarbonate and sulphates that do not cause hardness. For domestic treatment small base exchange equipment is available.

Water purification combines storage in reservoirs to allow suspended matter to settle, followed by filtration to remove both suspended and dissolved matter and a final treatment by chlorination.

Water mains: Water is supplied by the 'statutory water undertaker' required to supply a constant, potable (drinkable) supply of water for which service either a water rate is levied for domestic consumption or a charge by meter for most other users. The water rate is assessed on the rateable value of the premises and charged as a percentage of the value either half-yearly or annually. Metered supplies are charged at the current rate of the consumption recorded.

In many European countries the supply of water to all buildings is measured by meter and the cost charged by units of consumption. The advantage of making a charge through units of consumption is that it tends to encourage economy of consumption by the consumer who has a financial interest in maintaining his water installation. The disadvantage of metered supplies to the water authorities lies in the labour costs of periodic reading of meters and accounting for the actual consumption. It is open to any consumer in England to ask for a metered supply of water, providing the consumer bears the cost of fitting the meter.

Water is supplied, under pressure, through pipes laid under streets, roads or pavements. Cast iron, ductile iron, steel or concrete pipes are used. In urban areas duplicate trunk mains feed street mains. By closing valves individual lengths of main may be isolated for repairs and renewals without interrupting the supply.

Connections to water main – service pipe – supply pipe: Connections to the existing mains are made by

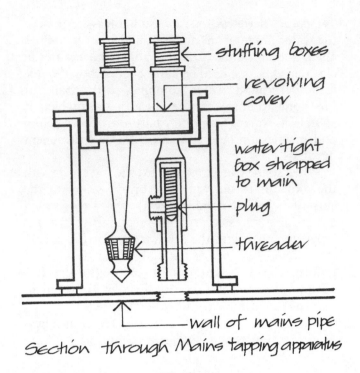

stuffing boxes

revolving cover

water-tight box strapped to main

plug

threader

wall of mains pipe

Section through Mains tapping apparatus

Fig. 3

the water undertaker. A stuffing box is clamped to the main, which is under pressure and a hole is drilled in the main and a plugged connection made as illustrated in Fig. 3. The house, or building service pipe connection is made to the ferrule cock on the crown of the main and the service pipe is run to a stop valve near to the site boundary of the building to be served. The stop valve is situated either immediately outside or inside the boundary. The purpose of the stop valve is to enable the water undertaker to disconnect the water supply where there is a waste of water in the building served, or non-payment of water rate or charge. The supply pipe is run underground and into the building as illustrated in Fig. 4. For convenience it is usual to run the supply pipe into the building through drain pipes to facilitate renewal of the pipe if need be.

It is the responsibility of the consumer to maintain the incoming service pipe on the consumer's land and that part of the pipe on the consumer's land and in his premises is termed a supply pipe.

At the point that the supply pipe enters the building there should be a stop valve (see Fig. 4), to disconnect the supply for repair and maintenance purposes.

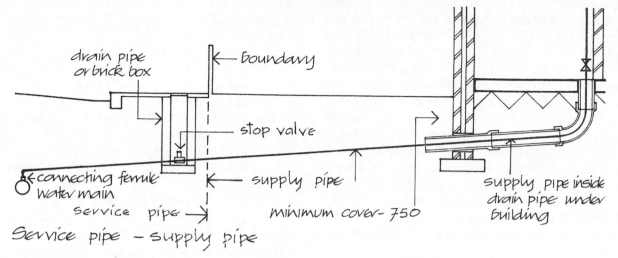

Fig. 4

To reduce the risk of freezing, the supply pipe should be laid at least 750 below the finished ground surface and if the supply pipe enters the building closer than 750 to the outside face of a wall, it should be insulated from the bottom of the bend where it rises into the building and up to the level of the ground floor.

History: Following the destruction of the Roman engineering works in Britain, there remained no organised piped supplies of water up to the twelfth century. In Saxon and Norman times the sole sources of supply were natural springs and man-made wells on which the small population depended and around which it settled.

During the twelfth and thirteenth centuries the monasteries organised supplies of water, usually from springs on high ground, from which water flowed by gravity, through wood, earthenware or lead pipes. Many of these monastic water systems were extended to supply neighbouring settlements. At that time water was less used, by the general population outside the monasteries, for either washing or drinking, than it is today.

With the dissolution of the monasteries in the sixteenth century the monastic water supplies were taken over by the civic authorities. The supply of water was generally in the hands of a local contractor who levied a charge for drawing water from the conduits and public fountains. This rudimentary system of water supply was in existence until the end of the seventeenth century, when the water wheel was first used to raise water to a cistern from which it flowed by gravity through wood or earthenware pipes to fountains, wash houses and buildings. The large wooden water wheels were driven by the river or stream from which they drew water, the wheel either scooping up water, which was discharged at a high level, or driving air pumps which forced the water up.

From the middle of the eighteenth century the Newcomen steam engine gradually replaced the water wheel as the motive power to raise water which was piped under pressure to communal conduits or fountains from which the populace drew their supply, and from which water carriers collected water to retail for a small charge. A few town houses had a piped supply of water, the charge for which was beyond the means of the majority. The supply of water was, by and large, in the hands of commercial suppliers for profit, and this arrangement continued up to the middle of the nineteenth century.

The rapid increase in the urban population that followed the Industrial Revolution, culminated in the spread of cholera epidemics during the first half of the nineteenth century. The prime cause of cholera was gross pollution of water supplies by untreated sewage discharged directly into rivers and streams from which water supplies were drawn. Following investigations of the cause of cholera and reports of the total inadequacy of water supplies for the urban population, principally by Edwin Chadwick, the Waterworks Clauses Act was passed in 1847.

The Waterworks Clauses Act was the first comprehensive Act that standardised waterwork practice throughout the country. The Act controlled the construction of waterworks, laying of pipes, supply of water, fouling of water and obliged the water undertakers to supply water constantly, in sufficient quantity and at a reasonable pressure to all houses demanding it. Prior to this Act the intermittent supply of water was a gravity supply, so that a storage cistern in each building was necessary to maintain a constant supply and those buildings above the level of the supply had no piped water. With a constant supply there was in theory no longer need for a storage cistern in each building and with reasonable pressure, piped water could be taken upstairs.

During the one hundred and thirty years following the Waterworks Clauses Act municipalities largely took over the supply of water. The control of water pollution improved dramatically and water undertakings expanded to supply the increasing urban population. This development of the supply and control of water supplies led to the Water Act 1973, which set up ten regional water authorities charged with the collection and supply of water in their area and the control of sewage treatment works and pollution of water.

The intermittent supply of water that was common from the middle of the eighteenth to the middle of the twentieth century necessitated the use of a water storage cistern in each building to maintain a constant supply. These cisterns were designed to contain one or more days' use of water in the building, to allow for interruption in the supply.

Since those days, most water undertakers in England have required consumers to install a water storage cistern for the supply of cold water in each building, even though the water authority is obliged by statute to provide a constant supply. The cistern usually provides storage for twelve to twenty-four hours' consumption.

In most European countries the use of cold water storage cisterns has long since been abandoned in favour of cold water supplied directly under pressure from the main supply on the grounds that roof level cisterns are 'expensive, unhygienic and unnecessary.'

Early in 1988 the new Water Supply Byelaws, based on the Model Water Byelaws 1986, will take effect. The water supply authorities in Great Britain will make byelaws based on the common Model Byelaws, so that there will be a common basis for the regulations covering the supply of water throughout the country.

In 1986 the Water Research Centre published the 'Water Supply Byelaws Guide' with the aim that it would assist those interested in understanding the byelaws based on the new model.

The guide, which runs to 220 pages, presumably sets out to explain the 101 byelaws by means of definition of terms, explanatory text and diagrams of water installations that conform to the provisions of the byelaws.

The Water Research Centre is run by the water authorities and the panel which produced the guide were mainly from the water authorities. All the indications are that the water authorities will, once the byelaws are made, do their level best to persuade consumers to adopt the now largely discredited system of storing water in a high level cistern. This view is confirmed by the examples given in considerable detail in the guide to the Model Byelaws, all of which illustrate the use of water storage cisterns as conforming to the byelaws and nowhere is there mention of mains pressure supplies, with the exception of unvented hot water storage cylinders, the use of which was permitted in the Building Regulations 1985.

The advantages of a mains pressure supply of water to all hot and cold water outlets in buildings are that there is a potable (drinkable) supply to all cold water outlets, a pressure supply to outlets such as showers, which do not produce a vigorous discharge from a roof cistern gravity feed and the abandonment of the roof level cold water storage cistern that is bulky and unnecessary.

The water authorities are required by statute to provide a constant supply of potable (drinkable) water, under pressure to all consumers on demand. There is, therefore, no need for a water storage cistern to provide a gravity feed of water in buildings.

On economic grounds there is very little difference in capital outlay between a roof level gravity feed cold water storage installation and a mains pressure installation, taking into account the check valves needed with the latter and probable greater maintenance costs of the mains pressure system owing to the necessity for regular testing of valves.

The one advantage of the roof level cistern is that there is an air gap between the highest water level in the cistern and the outlet from the mains supply that feeds it, which air gap is a very effective barrier to contaminated water in buildings flowing back into the mains, when pressure is reduced. This very simple and wholly effective barrier, an air gap, does not depend on moving parts and requires no maintenance whereas, the check valve, used in mains pressure installations, does depend on moving parts and requires maintenance if it is to be effective as a barrier to contamination of mains supply.

The purpose of the Water Supply Byelaws is to impose conditions to prevent waste of water or contamination of water.

In the Byelaws there is a definition of the terms 'supply pipe' and 'distributing pipe'. A supply pipe is any pipe, maintained by the consumer, that is subject to water pressure from the authorities' mains and a distributing pipe is any pipe (other than an overflow or flush pipe) that conveys water from a storage cistern or from hot water apparatus supplied from a feed cistern and under pressure from that cistern.

Prevention of waste of water is mainly concerned with the overflow of roof level cisterns and cisterns to W.C.s and bidets and the unnecessary use of water through faulty taps and installations. The byelaws can exercise no control over the waste of water through taps carelessly left running which is a prime cause of excessive consumption. At present most consumers pay a charge for water through a water rate that is levied annually as a percentage of rateable value, which takes no account of consumption. Where the charge for water is based on consumption measured by a meter, the consumer has a direct interest in the prevention of waste, through his pocket. A more sensible approach to prevention of waste would be through metered supplies, as is the practice in most continental European countries.

The principal concern of the byelaws is the prevention of contamination of mains supplied water by the flow of potentially polluted water from a supply or distributing system, back into the mains water supply.

Flow of water from a supply or distributing system in a building, back into the mains supply, can occur when there is loss of pressure in the mains due to failure of pumps, or work of repair and maintenance on the mains and also where a pumped supply in a building creates pressure greater than that in the mains.

The Water Byelaws Guide defines three principles of protection of mains supplied water services from the risk of contamination.

The first principle is that mains supplied water is kept separate from any other water such as water from a private source, non-potable water and water that has been drawn from a storage cistern.

This first line of defence against contamination of mains supplied water is through the air gap between the supply pipe and the water level in storage cisterns in gravity fed installations or the check valve (non-return valve) assembly between the service pipe and the supply pipe to mains pressure installations.

The second principle set out in the Model Byelaw Guide is that there should be no cross connections within an installation, for example from a supply pipe to a distributing pipe, so that potentially polluted water cannot reach the supply pipe, nor a pump be so connected as to cause backflow into the supply pipe. The byelaws that cover this aspect of prevention of contamination are directed to the prevention of backflow caused by booster pumps, by the use of check valves (non-return valves) and the prevention of contamination through the connection of a supply pipe to a closed circuit. This byelaw is concerned with the filling of primary water pipe circuits to boilers where the installation is fed by mains pressure, and the primary circuit has to be filled from the mains fed supply. A temporary connection is permitted for such filling through a double check valve assembly.

The third principle specified in the Model Water Byelaws Guide is protection against backflow from fittings, through draw off taps, flushing cisterns and washing machines. The concern here is that if, for example, a bath were to be overfilled and the pressure in the mains pressure supply pipe reduced, there would be a possibility that polluted water might find its way back into the mains pressure supply system. As a guard against this possibility, all draw off taps to baths, wash basins and sinks must either be fixed so that there is an air gap between the spill over level of the fitting and the outlet of the tap as illustrated in Fig. 5, or a double check valve assembly must be fitted to the supply pipe to each draw off tap.

These requirements apply equally to taps connected to mains pressure supply pipes and to distributing pipes from a cistern with the minor exemption of lowest draw off points. Plainly there is some small risk of backflow from a tap to a mains pressure supply pipe which is connected directly to the mains supply but it is difficult to see the risk involved to the

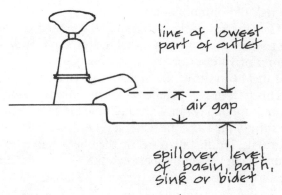

line of lowest
part of outlet

air gap

spillover level
of basin, bath,
sink or bidet

Air gap to taps to fittings

Fig. 5

mains supply where taps are connected to a cistern where the air gap disconnects the distributing pipe from the mains supply.

Similar provisions apply to shower hosepipes that can be lowered so that the head of the shower is below the spill over level of the fitting it serves. Here a double check valve assembly must be fitted to prevent backflow or backsiphonage.

The precautions necessary to prevent pollution from bidets are complicated by separate supplies of hot and cold water. Bidets that have taps that discharge over the rim are required to have an air gap or double check valve assembly similar to basins. Bidets fitted with ascending sprays, that is sprays that

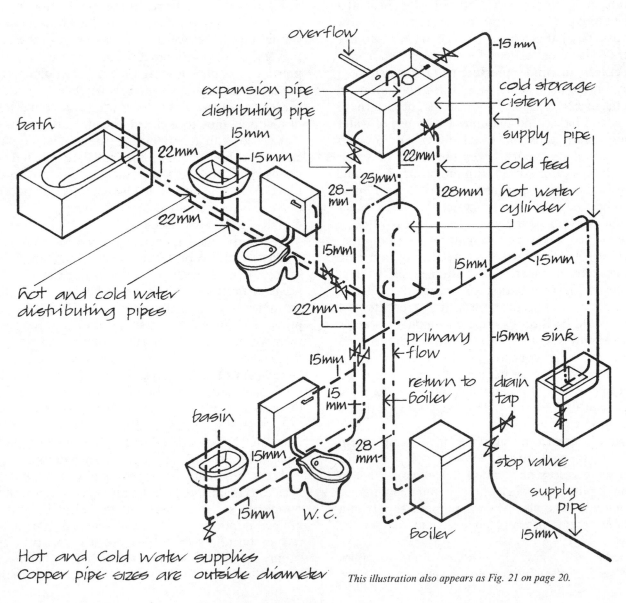

overflow

expansion pipe
distributing pipe

bath

15mm

22mm

15mm

28 mm

25mm

22mm

15mm

hot and cold water
distributing pipes

22mm

-15 mm

cold storage
cistern

supply pipe

cold feed

28mm

hot water
cylinder

15mm

15mm

primary
flow

15mm

return to
boiler

drain
tap

-15mm sink

basin

15mm

15
mm

28
mm

stop valve

15mm W.C.

boiler

supply
pipe

15mm

Hot and cold water supplies
Copper pipe sizes are outside diameter

This illustration also appears as Fig. 21 on page 20.

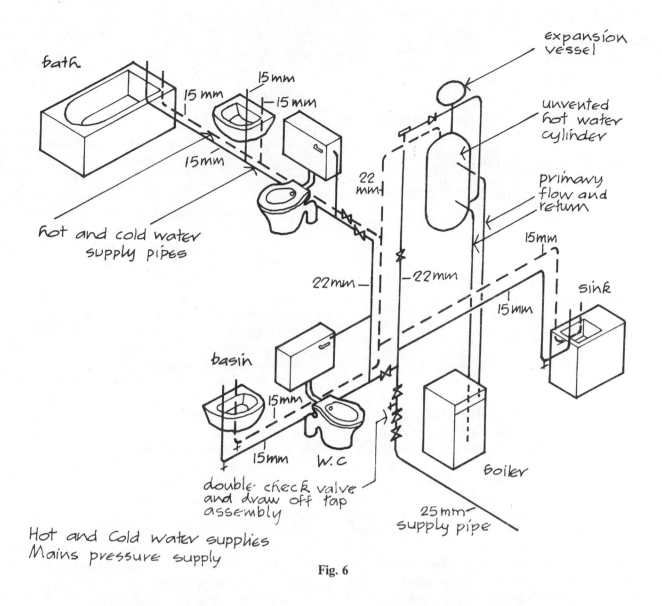

bath

15 mm

15 mm

15 mm

15mm

15mm

hot and cold water
supply pipes

expansion
vessel

unvented
hot water
cylinder

primary
flow and
return

22
mm

22mm

22mm

15mm

15mm

sink

basin

15mm

15mm

W.C

double check valve
and draw off tap
assembly

boiler

25mm
supply pipe

Hot and Cold water supplies
Mains pressure supply

Fig. 6

discharge upwards from the bowl of the bidet, are either connected to cisterns that are fed with hot and cold water, or the bidet is connected to separate distributing pipes with check valves.

It is in the two methods of prevention of backflow into the mains that the gravity feed and the mains pressure installations differ as illustrated in Fig. 6 and opposite.

It will be seen from the illustrations that the differences in these two systems lie in the water storage cistern and the extra pipework necessary to feed the roof level cistern and the distributing pipe from the cistern to the hot and cold water installations.

COLD WATER SERVICES

Mains supply pipe system: Fig. 6 illustrates the cold water, mains pressure pipe system to a two-storey house. Here the first line of defence against contamination of the mains supply is a double check valve assembly fitted upstream of the stop valve as the supply pipe enters the building.

A check valve, more commonly known as a non-return valve, is a simple, spring loaded valve that is designed to open one way to the pressure of water against the valve and to close when that pressure is reduced or stops. It, therefore, acts as a one way valve

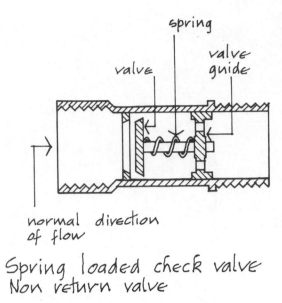

spring

valve

valve guide

normal direction of flow

Spring loaded check valve
Non return valve

Fig. 7

which closes against the direction of normal flow and prevents backflow from the supply pipe system into the mains. Fig. 7 is an illustration of a typical check valve.

A double check valve assembly is a combination of two check valves with a test cock between them. A test cock is a simple shut off device with a solid plug that, when rotated through ninety degrees, either opens or closes.

In use, a check valve may become coated with sediment, particularly in hard water areas, and not operate as it should. To test that the check valves are working and acting as non-return valves the stop valve is closed to test one check valve and opened to test the other with the test cock open.

The new Water Supply Byelaws will accept a check valve and vacuum breaker, a pipe interrupter or other fittings or arrangement of fittings designed to prevent backflow, as an alternative to a double check valve assembly.

From the double check valve assembly the mains pressure supply pipe rises and branches horizontally to supply fittings on each floor level with stop valves to isolate sections for repair or maintenance and drain plugs, in an arrangement similar to that for the cistern fed distribution pipe system. The supply pipe also supplies the unvented hot water storage cylinder.

Cold-water distributing pipe system: The term supply pipe is used to describe those pipes in a building which are under mains pressure. The term 'rising main' is also used in the same sense. A distributing pipe is one that carries water from a storage cistern, feed cistern or hot-water cylinder.

Most water undertakings in Britain have, until recently, required each building to have a cold-water storage cistern from which cold water is fed to all sanitary fittings and hot-water supply cylinders with the one exception of a single drinking water supply fed directly from the supply pipe and therefore the main to each house or flat. Fig 8 illustrates a supply pipe to a cold-water storage cistern and a drinking-water supply to a sink in a two-storey house.

The purpose of the cold-water storage cistern is to provide storage in each building equal to twelve to twenty-four hours' consumption, against interruption of supply during repair or maintenance work to the main. The storage cistern also relieves demand on the main during peak use periods, provides a constant supply of water with limited pressures in distributing pipes and reduces noise and wear on fittings. The storage cistern also limits back siphonage of water from fittings into the main. The disadvantages of the storage cistern are that it is bulky and has to be fitted into the roof space where it has to be protected from frost and the pipework to a storage cold-water system is more extensive than a main supply cold-water system.

When the new Water Supply Byelaws come into effect, early in 1988, it will be open to any consumer to use a mains pressure cold water and hot water supply system to all outlets in buildings. In place of a gravity fed distributing system there will be a mains pressure supply system as illustrated in Fig. 6.

Cold-water storage cistern: A cistern is a water storage container which is open to the air and in which water is at normal atmospheric pressure. Cisterns are usually manufactured from mild steel plate or sheet, welded or rivetted together and galvanised after manufacture. Fig. 9 illustrates a typical galvanised steel cistern. The cistern has a turnover flanged top, or angle section stiffener and

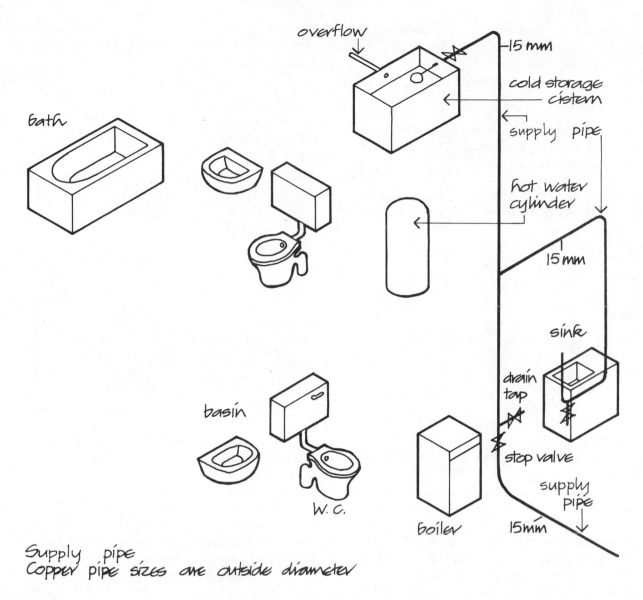

Fig. 8

corner plates, as illustrated, to stiffen the sides against water pressure. A loose steel cover protects the water from contamination by dust and dirt. Alternatively, an insulating top may be used. In course of time these galvanised steel cisterns may rust and need replacing every twenty or thirty years. To replace an existing cistern it may well be necessary to cut away a ceiling to get the new cistern into the roof space. As an alternative two or more cisterns small enough to pass through the trap door may be used or the cold distribution connected directly to the service pipe, which was contrary to most water undertakers

regulations. In recent years plastic, asbestos cement and glassfibre cisterns have been used. These materials do not rust but are not so robust as steel and need more careful handling. Fig. 10, is an illustration of these cisterns.

The cold-water storage cistern must be fixed not less than two metres above the highest fitting it is to supply with water. The most convenient place for it is therefore in the space below a pitched roof, in a tank room or chamber above a flat roof or at some high level below the roof. In whichever position the cistern is fixed there must be space around and over the cistern for maintenance or replacement of the valve. Fig. 11 illustrates a cold-water storage cistern on timber spreaders.

The capacity of the cold-water storage cistern is usually 114 litres per dwelling where the cistern supplies cold taps and W.C.s and 227 litres per dwelling for both cold and domestic hot water. An alternative is to calculate the capacity of the storage cistern at 90 litres per resident.

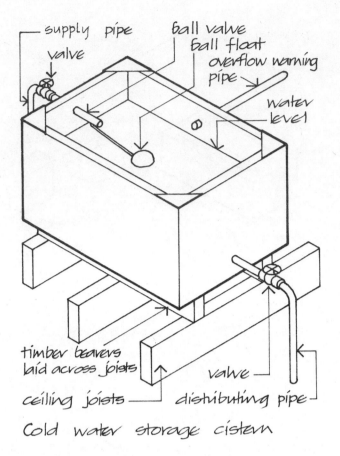

Cold water storage cistern

Fig. 11

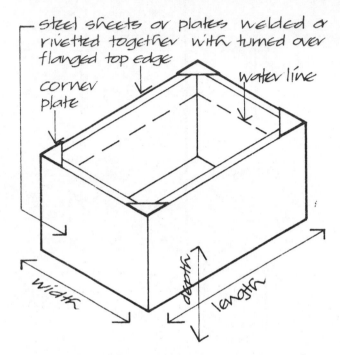

Capacity to water line - 18 to 3364 litres available in the following dimensions
Length - 457 to 2438 mm
width - 305 to 1524 mm
depth - 305 to 1219 mm.

Galvanised steel cistern

Fig. 9

To prevent contamination of water by backsiphonage, backflow or cross connection the new Water Supply Byelaws that come into force in 1988 require an air gap between the outlet of float valves to cisterns and the highest water level in the cistern. This air gap is related to the bore of the supply pipe or the outlet as set out in Table 1, page 35, and is taken as the minimum distance between the outlet of the float valve and the highest water level when the overflow

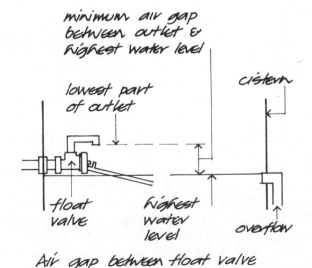

Air gap between float valve outlet & highest water level

Fig. 12

12

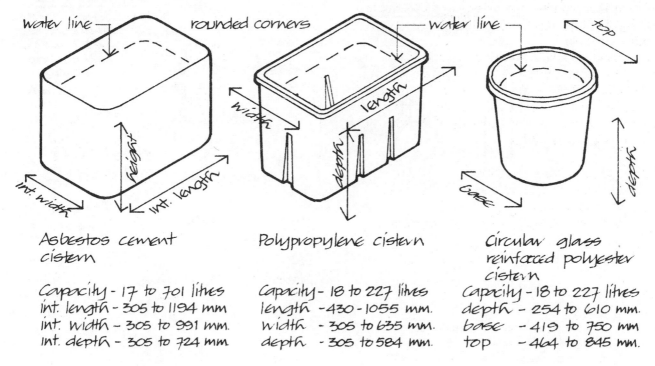

Asbestos cement cistern

Capacity - 17 to 701 litres
Int. length - 305 to 1194 mm
Int. width - 305 to 991 mm.
Int. depth - 305 to 724 mm

Polypropylene cistern

Capacity - 18 to 227 litres
length - 430 - 1055 mm.
width - 305 to 635 mm.
depth - 305 to 584 mm.

Circular glass reinforced polyester cistern

Capacity - 18 to 227 litres
depth - 254 to 610 mm.
base - 419 to 750 mm
top - 464 to 845 mm.

Fig. 10

pipe is passing the maximum rate of inflow to the cistern. If the overflow pipe is adequately sized, the highest water level will be at the top of the overflow pipe. Fig. 12 is an illustration of the air gap necessary to float valves to cisterns.

Ball valve: The supply pipe is run up inside the building, preferably away from external walls to avoid the possibility of freezing, and is connected to the cistern through a stop valve to disconnect the supply for rewashering or renewal of the ball valve. The water supply to the cistern is controlled by a ball valve which is fixed to the cistern above the water line as illustrated in Fig. 11. A hollow copper or plastic ball which floats on the water activates the valve. As water is drawn the float falls, opens the valve to let water in and as the float rises it closes the valve. The three types of valve in use are the Croydon, the Portsmouth and the Diaphragm or BRS valve, the Diaphragm being used for most new installations. Figs. 13, 14 and 15 illustrate these three valves. It will be seen that the piston of the Croydon valve moves vertically and the Portsmouth horizontally. The Croydon valve is noisy in operation and is little used today.

The original Portsmouth valve has been refined so that the piston is under equal water pressure at both ends to reduce noise of operation. The Diaphragm valve is quiet in operation and gives good service through the nylon nozzle and the rubber diaphragm. The outlet tube shown in Fig. 15 provides silent filling through the nozzles that discharge water in jets above the water level in the cistern.

Overflow warning pipe: As a precaution against failure of the valve, and consequent overflow of the cistern, most water undertakers require an overflow warning pipe to be connected to the cistern above the water line and carried out of the building to discharge where the overflow of water will give obvious warning. The overflow pipe should be of larger bore than the service pipe to the cistern and preferably twice the bore of the service pipe and not less than 19 bore.

Insulation: The Water Supply Byelaws that will come into effect early in 1988 include a requirement that water storage cisterns be insulated and fitted with a close fitting cover that excludes light and insects and is not airtight and that the cistern shall be

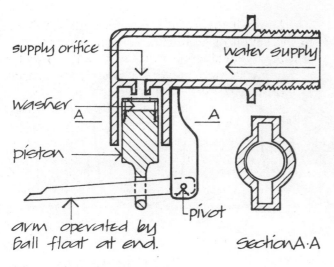

supply orifice

water supply

washer

A ———— A

piston

arm operated by ball float at end.

Section A·A

Croydon ball valve

pivot

Fig. 13

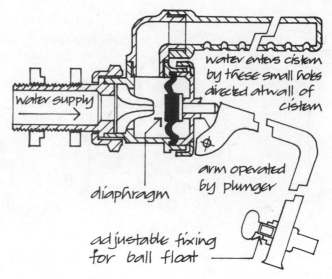

water supply

water enters cistern by these small holes directed at wall of cistern

diaphragm

arm operated by plunger

adjustable fixing for ball float

Diaphragm ball valve

Fig. 15

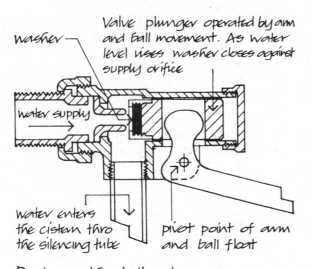

washer

Valve plunger operated by arm and ball movement. As water level rises washer closes against supply orifice

water supply

water enters the cistern thro the silencing tube

pivot point of arm and ball float

Portsmouth ball valve

Fig. 14

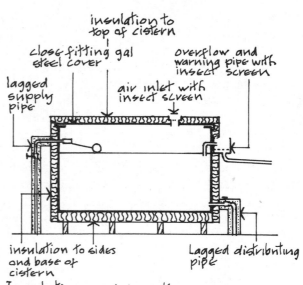

insulation to top of cistern

close fitting gal steel cover

overflow and warning pipe with insect screen

lagged supply pipe

air inlet with insect screen

insulation to sides and base of cistern

Lagged distributing pipe

Insulation and insect screens to cold water storage cistern

Fig. 16

adequately supported to avoid distortion and be in a position where it may be readily inspected and cleaned, and valves readily installed, renewed or adjusted.

To meet these requirements it will be necessary to fit cisterns on a platform to support the cistern and spread its load to ceiling or roof rafters. The cistern should be surrounded with adequate insulation in the form of quilted or board insulation, strapped or otherwise securely fixed. The thickness of the insulation is not specified as it will depend on the position in which the cistern is fixed. Cisterns which are fixed

inside the roof space under pitched roofs, where the insulation is at ceiling level and the roof space ventilated to minimise condensation, will require heavy, airtight insulation against freezing. The cover to the cistern will have to be insulated as will the base of the cistern where it is not in direct contact with some other insulation.

Fig. 16 is an illustration of a cistern with cover and insulation. The air inlet shown in the airtight cover has an insect screen as does the overflow pipe.

Distributing pipe system: Fig. 17 illustrates the cold-water distributing pipe system for a two-storey house. It will be seen that the distributing pipe is connected to the cistern some 50 mm above the bottom of the cistern to prevent any sediment that may have collected, entering the pipe. A stop valve is fitted to the pipe adjacent to the cistern, isolating the whole system from the cistern in the event of repairs and renewals. The distributing pipe is carried down inside the building with horizontal branches to the first-floor and ground-floor fittings as shown in Fig.

17. The aim in the layout of the pipework is economy in the length of pipe runs, and on this depends a sensible layout of sanitary fittings. In Fig. 17 it will be seen that one horizontal branch serves both bath, basin and W.C. For rewashering taps, stop valves are fitted to branches as shown. Where one branch serves three fittings as shown in Fig. 17 then one stop valve will serve to isolate all three fittings.

Drain or emptying plugs should be provided where pipework cannot be drained to taps so that the whole distributing system may be drained for renewal or repair of pipework or when a building is left empty and water in the system might otherwise freeze and fracture pipework or joints.

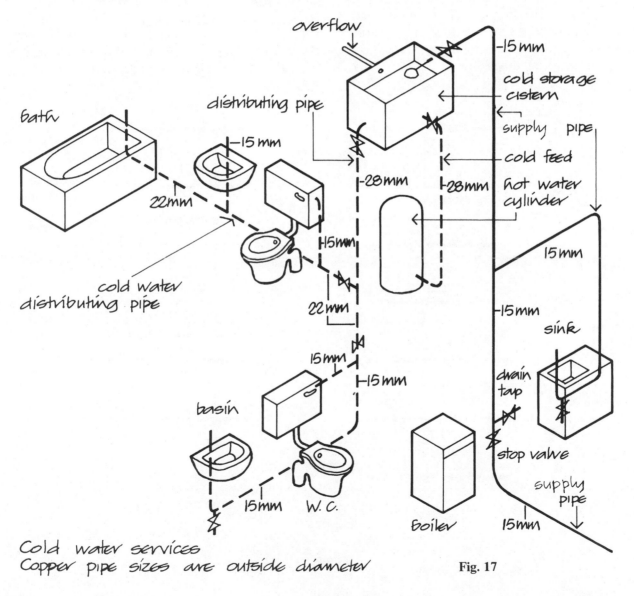

Cold water services
Copper pipe sizes are outside diameter

Fig. 17

HOT-WATER SERVICES

There are two hot-water supply systems, the central and the local. In the former, water is heated and stored centrally for general distribution and in the latter water is heated, or heated and stored locally for local use. The difference between these systems is that with the central system hot water is run to the site of the sanitary appliances from a central heat source, and with the local system the heat source, gas or electricity, is run to the local heater which is adjacent to the sanitary appliances. Fig. 18 illustrates the two systems diagrammatically.

The central system is suited, for example, to houses, hotels, offices and flats where a central boiler fired by solid fuel, oil, gas or electricity heats water in bulk for distribution through a straightforward vertical distributing pipe system with short draw-off branches leading to taps to sanitary appliances on each floor. In large buildings, one heat source may serve two or more hot-water storage cylinders to avoid excessively long distribution pipe runs.

The local system is used for local washing facilities where the fuel, gas or electricity is run to the local heater either to avoid extensive, and, therefore, uneconomic supply or distributing pipe runs or where local control is an advantage.

In some buildings it may be economic to use a combination of central and local hot-water systems.

Central hot-water supply: From Fig. 18 it will be seen that water is heated and stored in a central cylinder from which it circulates around a distributing pipe system from which hot water is drawn. The storage cylinder contains hot water sufficient for both anticipated peak demand and demands during the recharge period. The system is therefore designed to supply hot water on demand at all times. The one disadvantage of the system is that there is some loss of heat from the distributing pipes no matter how

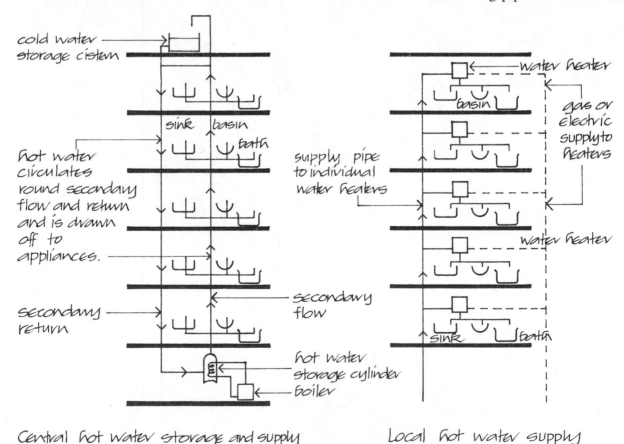

Central hot water storage and supply   Local hot water supply

Fig. 18

adequately they are insulated. This is outweighed by the economy and convenience of one central heat source that can be fired by the cheapest fuel available, and one hot water source to install, supply and maintain – hot water being at hand constantly by simply turning a tap.

Where a mains pressure supply system is used the supply pipe connects to the unvented hot water storage cylinder from which supply pipes connect to the fittings and there is no roof level storage cistern.

Local hot-water supply: A water heater adjacent to the fittings to be supplied is fired by gas or electricity run to the site of the heater. Fuel for local heaters is generally confined to gas or electricity. The water is either heated and stored locally or heated instantaneously as it flows through the heater. The advantages of this system are that there is a minimum of distributing pipework, initial outlay is comparatively low and the control and payment for fuel can be local, an advantage, for example, to the landlord of residential flats. The disadvantage is that local heaters are appreciably more expensive to run and maintain than one central system.

Unvented mains pressure hot water storage cylinder: The requirements for hygiene set out in The Building Regulations 1985 detail some of the precautions for safety in the use of unvented hot water storage systems and the Water Supply Byelaws that will come into effect in 1988 set out requirements for mains pressure supplies to unvented systems.

To date, hot water systems, other than instantaneous heaters, have been supplied by water from a storage cistern from which the system was vented by means of an expansion pipe as illustrated in Fig. 21. Once the new Byelaws are in operation it will be permitted to use the system of unvented secondary hot water supply that has been in use in Europe and North America for many years.

The difference between the traditional vented hot water system and the unvented system is that in the former, expansion of hot water is accommodated by the vented expansion pipe that will discharge an excess of expansion water to the cistern and in the unvented system expansion of hot water is relieved by an expansion vessel which contains a cushion of gas or air sufficient to take up the expansion by compression of the gas.

The advantages of the unvented over the vented

hot water system, for the user, lie in the improved flow rates from showers and also taps, reduction in noise caused by the filling of storage cisterns and virtually no risk of frost damage. There is little if any economic advantage in the use of the unvented system. The saving in eliminating the cistern, feed and expansion pipes is offset by the additional cost of the expansion vessel and temperature and expansion control valves and the necessary, comparatively frequent, maintenance of these controls.

Overleaf is an illustration of an unvented hot water cylinder and hot water supply system to a small house. Fig. 19 is a diagram of the controls required for an unvented hot water storage cylinder and Fig. 20 an illustration of a packaged cylinder. The pressure relief valve shown in the feed pipe is a safety device against the expansion vessel being unable to take up the whole of the expansion of heated water and as a relief should the feed pressure rise.

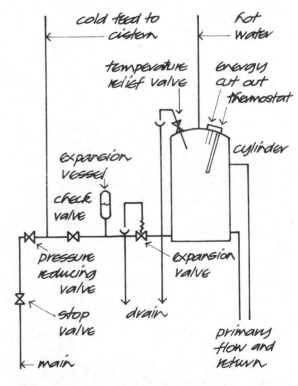

Diagram of low pressure unvented hot water system

Fig. 19

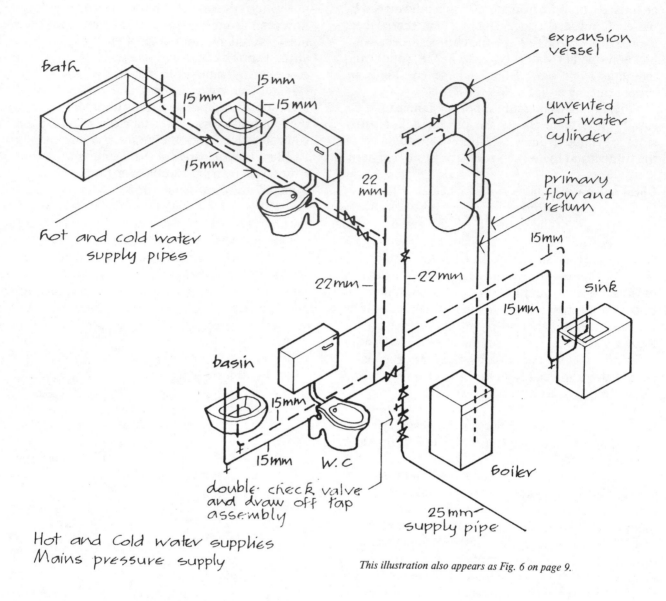

bath

15 mm

15 mm

15 mm

15 mm

hot and cold water
supply pipes

22
mm

expansion
vessel

unvented
hot water
cylinder

primary
flow and
return

15mm

sink

22mm

22mm

15mm

basin

15mm

15mm   W.C

double check valve
and draw off tap
assembly

boiler

25mm
supply pipe

Hot and Cold water supplies
Mains pressure supply

This illustration also appears as Fig. 6 on page 9.

For control against overheating there is a thermostat on the immersion heater and also a temperature limiting cut out that operates on the electricity supply and a temperature operated relief valve to discharge if the other controls fail.

The pressure reducing valve is fitted to the feed pipe where low pressure systems are used and is provided to reduce mains pressure to a level that the cylinder can safely withstand. Where high pressure systems are used and the cylinder is designed to stand high pressure, then the pressure relief valve is omitted.

Central hot-water systems: Fig. 21 is an illustration of a central hot-water system for a two-storey house. It will be seen that the boiler is connected through primary flow and return pipes to the heat exchanger in the hot-water storage cylinder. The cold-water storage cistern provides a supply through a cold feed to the cylinder from which distributing pipes carry hot water to the draw-off branches to the sanitary appliances. The flow pipe is carried up, with an open end over the cistern, so that in the event of overheating, steam and water may escape. An electric immersion heater is fitted to the hot-water storage

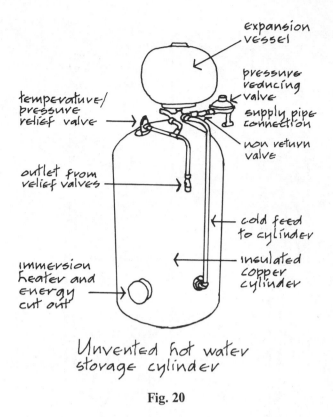

expansion vessel

pressure reducing valve

temperature/pressure relief valve

supply pipe connection

non return valve

outlet from relief valves

cold feed to cylinder

immersion heater and energy cut out

insulated copper cylinder

Unvented hot water storage cylinder

Fig. 20

cylinder to provide hot water when the boiler is not used for space heating. Stop valves and drain cocks are fitted to the pipe system for the reasons given for cold-water pipe systems.

Hot-water boiler or heater: For a small building such as the two-storey house illustrated in Fig. 21 it is general practice to utilise one boiler for both space heating and hot water, to economise in the initial outlay on heating equipment and pipework and to make maximum use of floor space. The disadvantage of a combined space heating and hot-water boiler is that in mild weather in winter months the water temperature required for space heating is lower than that reasonable for hot water. For separate control of temperature for space heating and hot water it is advantageous to have separate hot water and space heating boilers.

An electric immersion heater is both an inefficient and an expensive means of heating water. Because of the comparatively small surface area of the immersion heater, it requires some four hours to heat the water in the cylinder as compared to two hours for the heat exchange coil from the boiler. This slow recharge rate is an inconvenience added to the high cost of electricity.

The boilers, whether combined space heating and hot water or separate may be fired by solid fuel, gas, oil or electricity, and as set down are in order of current costs, solid fuel being cheapest. Solid fuel suffers the disadvantage of being bulky to store and residual ash and clinker are time-consuming and dirty to clear. Oil requires a bulky storage container and tends to smell, while gas is the most convenient of the fuels. Electricity is less used because of its cost.

The temperature of the water heated by the boiler is controlled by a thermostat, which can be set by hand to a range of water temperatures from 65°C to 85°C, the boiler firing and cutting out as the water temperature falls and then rises to the preselected temperature.

Water heated in the boiler rises in the primary flow pipe to the heat exchange coil or container inside the hot-water storage cylinder and as it exchanges its heat through the exchanger to the water in the cylinder it cools and returns through the primary return pipe back to the boiler for reheating. There is a gravity circulation of water in the primary pipe system. The primary flow and return pipes should be as short as practicable, that is, the cylinder should be near the boiler to minimise loss of heat from the pipes. The circulating pipes from the boiler through the heat exchanger are termed primary flow and return as they convey the primary source of heat in the hot-water system.

A small feed cistern provides the head of water required for the boiler and its pipe system. Stop valves are fitted as shown in Fig. 21 to isolate parts of the system for repairs or renewals.

Vented hot-water storage cylinder: The hot-water storage cylinder is designed to contain water under pressure of the head of water from the cold-water storage cistern. Most hot-water storage containers are cylindrical and are fixed vertically to encourage cold water fed into the lower part of the cylinder to rise, as it is heated by the heat exchanger, to the top of the cylinder from which hot water is drawn and so minimise mixing of cold and hot water. The cold-feed pipe to the cylinder is run from the cold-water storage cistern and connected through an isolating stop valve to the base of the cylinder. The hot-water distributing pipe is run from the top of the cylinder to the draw-off branches to sanitary appliances and carried up to discharge over the cold cistern, in case of overheating, as illustrated in Fig. 21.

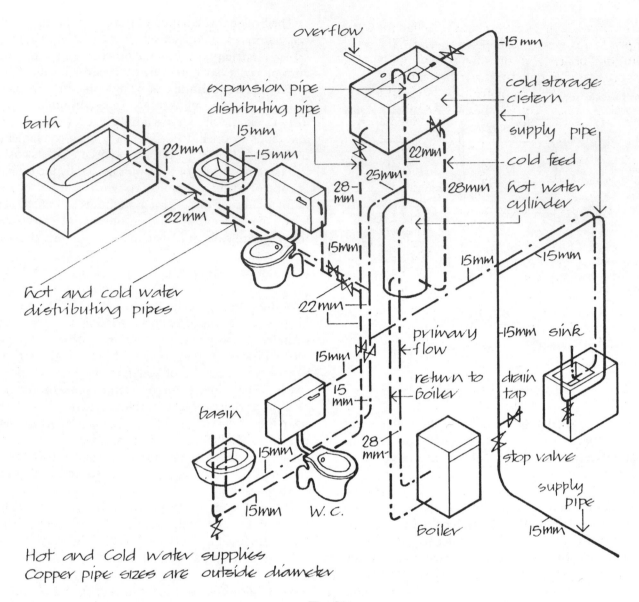

overflow

-15 mm

expansion pipe
distributing pipe

cold storage
cistern

supply pipe

15mm

cold feed

22mm

-15mm

hot water
cylinder

bath

28-
mm

25mm

28mm

22mm

hot and cold water
distributing pipes

15mm

15mm

15mm

15mm

22mm

primary
flow

-15mm sink

15mm

return to
boiler

drain
tap

15
mm

basin

15mm

stop valve

28
mm

supply
pipe

15mm W. C.

boiler

15mm

Hot and Cold water supplies
Copper pipe sizes are outside diameter

Fig. 21

The required storage capacity of the cylinder depends on the number of sanitary appliances to be served and the estimated demand. A limited experiment by the Building Research Station suggests that the average consumption of domestic hot water is in the region of 50 litres per person per day. The interval between times of maximum demand on domestic hot water are longer than the recovery period required to reheat water in storage systems, and it is reasonable, therefore, to provide hot-water storage capacity of 50 to 60 litres per person.

Storage cylinders are made either of galvanised sheet steel or copper sheet welded or riveted. Fig. 22

is an illustration of typical hot-water storage cylinders. In course of time galvanised steel cylinders rust and their average life is about twenty years whereas a copper cylinder may have an unlimited life. Which of these two is used will depend on the pressure of the head of cold water from the cistern, the nature of the water and pipework used and initial cost considerations. Steel cylinders can support greater water pressure than copper cylinders and steel cylinders are appreciably cheaper than copper cylinders.

The hot-water storage cylinders illustrated in Fig. 22 are indirect cylinders, so called because the primary hot water from the boiler exchanges its heat indirectly through a heat exchanger to the hot-water supply, there being no connection between the water from the boiler and the hot-water supply. The purpose of this indirect transfer of heat is to avoid drawing hot water directly from the water system of the boiler. Where hot water is drawn directly from the boiler it has to be replaced and in hard water areas each fresh charge of water will deposit scale inside the boiler and its pipework and in time the build up of scale will reduce the efficiency of the boiler and the bore of its pipes. With an indirect cylinder there is no replacement of water to the boiler and its primary pipes and therefore no build up of scale. Scale formation is proportional to water temperature. There is lesser build up of scale in the secondary hot-water circulation because of the lower water temperature in the system. Indirect cylinders are in addition a protection against the possibility of drawing scalding water directly from the boiler. For these reasons indirect cylinders are generally used.

An electric immersion heater is a form of direct heating of the hot-water supply. In hard water areas the heater will become coated with scale and lose efficiency.

A direct hot-water storage cylinder takes and stores hot water directly from the boiler, and draw off water for fittings is taken directly from this source.

Some solid fuel open fires and stoves are fitted with back boilers to provide hot water as well as space heating (see Vol. 2). The water heated by the back boiler is stored in a cylinder from which hot water is drawn directly.

The secondary hot water pipe system illustrated in Fig. 21 is vented to the storage cistern through an expansion pipe that discharges over the cistern. The expansion pipe is a precaution against overheating of water in the secondary system and consequent expansion of water that could then discharge to the cistern.

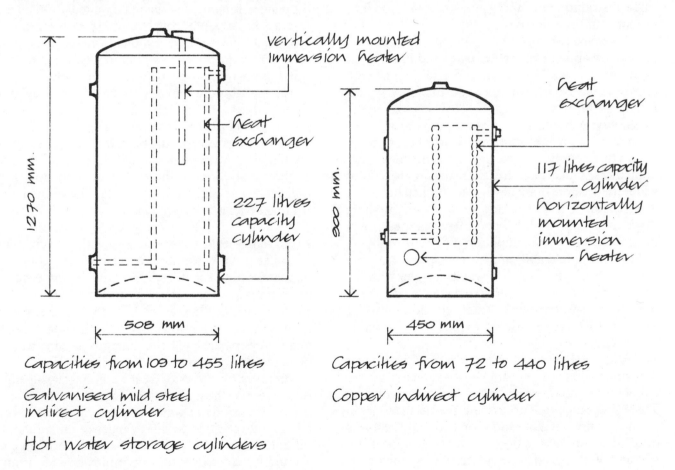

Capacities from 109 to 455 litres

Galvanised mild steel indirect cylinder

Hot water storage cylinders

Capacities from 72 to 440 litres

Copper indirect cylinder

Fig. 22

Hot-water distributing and supply pipe systems: Hot water may be drawn directly through short branches from a single distributing or supply pipe connected to the hot-water storage cylinder or water heater, or from flow and return distributing or supply pipes in which hot water circulates from and back to the storage cylinder as illustrated in Fig. 18. With the single pipe draw-off system illustrated in Figs. 18 and 21 there is little circulation of hot water in the pipes when water is not being drawn so that the water loses heat. When taps are opened to draw water, the cooled water in the pipes has to be run off before hot water can be drawn. Where pipe lengths are short the discharge of cooled water is a slight inconvenience and there is a small waste of water. With longer pipe runs there is appreciable inconvenience in delay and waste of water before reasonably hot water is to hand. In small buildings and for local hot-water supplies in large buildings where the sanitary appliances are close to the hot-water source, the single distributing or supply pipe system is economic in initial and running costs.

Where pipe runs from hot-water storage cylinders to sanitary appliances are extensive and drawing off cooled water would take an appreciable time with consequent waste of water, a circulating pipe system is used as illustrated in Fig. 18. Hot water circulates by gravity or by pressure from a pump around the circulating pipe system from which hot water is drawn through short single pipe branches to sanitary appliances. Once taps are opened and the cooled water in the short branches is run off, then hot water is at hand. The circulating pipe system is more expensive in initial outlay and there is a greater loss of heat because of the duplicate pipe runs.

Both the single and circulating pipe systems are run from the top of the hot-water cylinder with the single pipe and the flow pipe carried up to discharge over the cold-water storage cistern to allow escape of steam and water in case of overheating in vented systems.

The single pipe distributing or supply system and the short single pipe draw-off branches to the circulating system, are described as dead legs of pipe. These single pipe runs are so described as the water in them does not circulate and soon cools and becomes dead. To minimise waste of water resulting from running off this dead leg of water, it is recommended that dead leg pipes should not exceed 12 metres for pipes not exceeding 20 mm, 7.6 m for pipes not exceeding 25 mm, 3 m for pipes not exceeding 25 mm and 1 m for pipes serving spray tap. For rewashering of taps, stop valves are fitted to draw-off branches as illustrated in Figs 6 and 21.

Insulation: To conserve heat it is practice to insulate the hot-water storage cylinder, the primary flow and return pipes, and the secondary distributing or supply circulating systems. A range of preformed linings and jackets is available for standard-size cylinders and preformed linings for pipes.

In multi-storey buildings the central system of hot-water storage and distribution is similar, in principle, to that illustrated in Fig. 18. A central boiler heats water which is stored centrally and is pumped through a secondary circulation from which short dead leg draw-off branches connect to sanitary appliances.

In extensive and tall buildings there will be appreciable loss of heat and consequent temperature drop along long runs of secondary circulation pipes. It may be advantageous to utilise two or more cylinders, each heated by the primary flow and return from the boiler to maintain a reasonable hot-water temperature throughout the building.

The one or more central hot-water storage cylinders for large buildings are of economic advantage in initial, running and maintenance costs where the building owner accepts the responsibility for supplying hot water without a separate charge to each user of the supply. Where the building owner does not undertake to supply hot water then one of the local heating systems is used.

Local water-heating systems: Hot water is run from a heater to the sanitary appliance or group of appliances to be served. Local water heating systems are employed where the user bears the cost of heating as in residential flats and where there are isolated groups of sanitary appliances as in factories, shops and houses where long circulating pipe runs would be uneconomic in initial and running costs.

There are two types of local water heater, the hot-water storage heater and the instantaneous water heater. The local hot-water storage heater consists of a heat source and a storage cylinder or tank and the instantaneous heater a heat source through or around which cold water runs and is heated instantaneously as it is run off. These two types of heater are illustrated in Fig. 23.

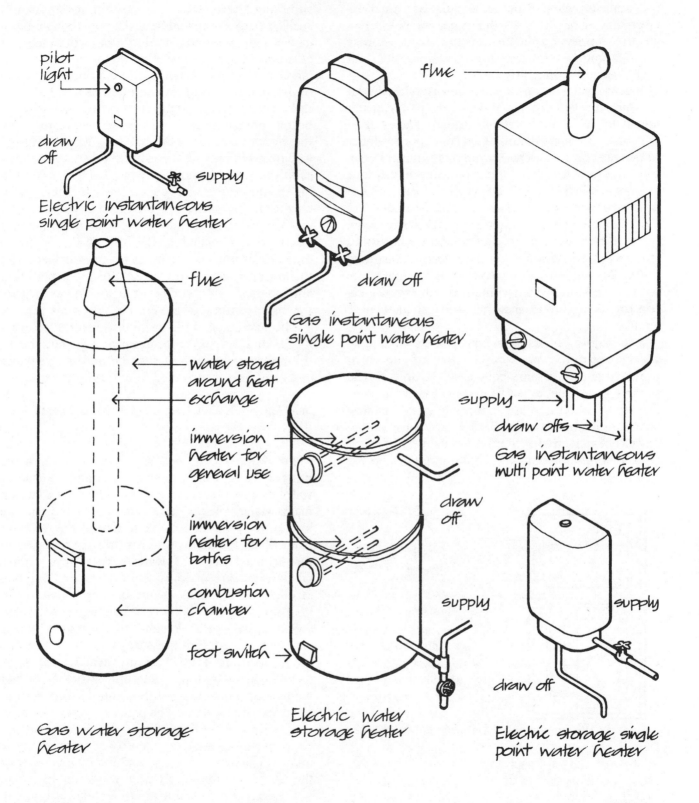

pilot light

draw off

supply

Electric instantaneous single point water heater

flue

water stored around heat exchange

immersion heater for general use

immersion heater for baths

combustion chamber

foot switch

Gas water storage heater

flue

draw off

Gas instantaneous single point water heater

draw off

supply

Electric water storage heater

supply

draw offs

Gas instantaneous multi point water heater

supply

draw off

Electric storage single point water heater

Fig. 23

Local hot-water storage heaters are fired by electricity or gas. In the former, heating is from an electric immersion heater in the water storage cylinder and in the latter from pipe coils or a heat exchanger surrounded by water.

Electric water storage heaters consist of a cylinder in which the water is heated by an immersion heater and from which hot water is drawn. The cylinder may be a standard galvanised steel or copper cylinder or one of the purpose-made cylinders as illustrated in Fig. 23. The cold-water supply to local water storage heaters is taken from the cold-water storage cistern or from a mains pressure supply pipe. Typical water storage heaters are illustrated in Fig. 23. There are on the market, water heaters that combine a hot-water storage heater and water storage cistern as illustrated in Fig. 24. These are designed for use in conversions of large buildings to self-contained flats where local control of the cold-water storage and water heating is an advantage.

The majority of instantaneous heaters operate by gas there being a combustion chamber around which water circulates in pipe coils as it is run off. The smaller instantaneous gas heaters are for single-point delivery of water and are commonly known as sink heaters as ilustrated in Fig. 23. The larger instantaneous gas heaters are for multi-point delivery of water and are commonly known as multi-point heaters for supplying water to a range of sanitary appliances such as a sink, basin and bath. The small single-point gas heater does not need a flue when there is adequate permanent ventilation to the room. The larger multi-point heaters require a flue in the form of a connection to an existing flue or to a balanced flue taken to the outside air. Instantaneous gas-water heaters are connected to the water service pipe and therefore operate at mains pressure. Mains pressure is required to operate the valve that turns on the gas supply as water is run. Gas water heaters operate at high temperatures and require fairly frequent maintenance if they are to operate efficiently.

There are electrically operated instantaneous water heaters available. Because of the technical difficulty of transferring heat energy from electricity to flowing water these heaters are both inefficient and have a slow water discharge rate and as they are expensive to run they are used less than gas heaters.

The advantage of the instantaneous heater is that it is less bulky than the storage heater. Instantaneous heaters are expensive in running and maintenance costs and have a restricted rate of run-off water.

WATER SERVICES TO MULTI-STOREY BUILDINGS

Mains water is supplied under pressure from the head of water from a reservoir or pumped head of water or a combination of both. The level to which mains water will rise in a building depends on the level of the building relative to that of the reservoir from which the mains water is drawn or relative to the artificial head of water created by pumps. Obviously mains pressure will rise less in a building on high ground than in one on lower ground. In built-up areas there will at peak times, such as early morning, be a peak demand on the mains supply, resulting in reduced pressure available from the water main. It is the pressure available at peak demand times that will determine whether or not mains supply pressure is sufficient to feed cold-water to upper water outlets. The pressure available varies from place to place depending on natural or artificial water pressure available, intensity of demand on the main at peak demand time and the relative level of the building to the supply pressure available.

Fig. 25 is an illustration of an eight-storey building where the mains pressure at peak demand time is sufficient to feed all cold and hot water outlets on all

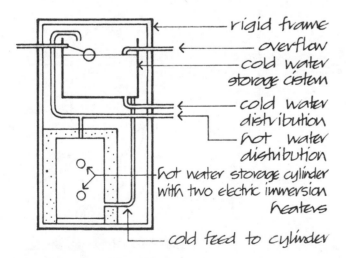

Combined cold and hot water storage unit.

Fig. 24

floors. It will be seen that the supply pipe branches to feed water outlets on each floor.

Where there is a common supply of water to several floors in a building it is necessary to make allowances for the loss of residual pressure and reduced flows as the common supply pipe serves successive floors, either up or down the building. Normal design technique is to reduce the diameter of the pipes to compensate for the reduced pressures and reduced flows to provide a reasonable equality of flow from taps on each floor.

Where main pressure is sufficient to provide a supply to a multi-storey building it is not always possible to provide a reasonable equality of flow to each floor by varying pipe sizes alone. The use of two or more supply pipes to each floor, each serving a group of fittings on each floor, to spread the demand on the supply, is common practice. Fig. 26 illustrates the rising supply pipes to each floor of a multi-storey building with reduction in pipe size along the flow to provide reasonable equality of flow from taps on each floor.

In some European countries a reasonable rate of flow from taps on all floors is a prime consideration. One method of working towards this aim is to use pressure reducing valves at each floor level to control pressure and so equalise the flow, floor by floor.

Another method that is being used experimentally is the use of multiple rising pipes as illustrated in Fig. 27. It will be seen that one rising supply pipe branches to supply the three lower floors and then rises to supply the three floors above where it is joined and its supply reinforced by the second rising supply and then up to the top three floors where it is joined and reinforced by the third rising supply pipe. The diameter of the rising pipes varies to produce a reasonable uniformity of flow to each floor. Plainly this system can best be utilised where fittings can be closely grouped around a duct in which the multiple risers are housed.

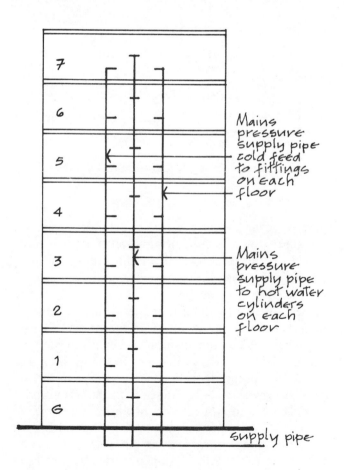

Fig. 25

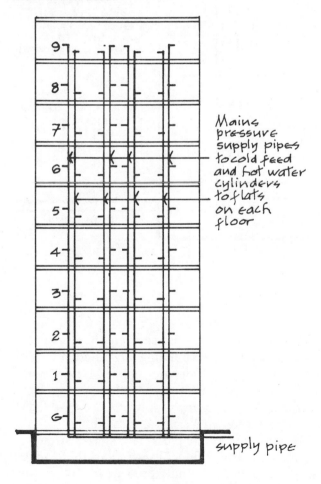

Fig. 26

Where mains pressure is insufficient, at peak demand times, to raise water to the highest water outlet it is necessary to install pumps in the building to raise water to the higher water outlets. In this situation it is usual to supply those outlets that the mains pressure will reach, from the supply pipe and those above by the pumped supply to limit the load on the pumps as illustrated in Fig. 28.

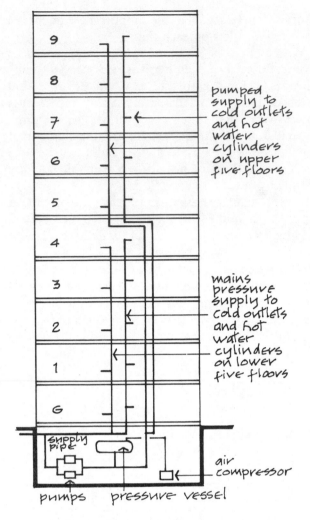

pumped supply to cold outlets and hot water cylinders on upper five floors

mains pressure supply to cold outlets and hot water cylinders on lower five floors

supply pipe

pumps   pressure vessel

air compressor

Fig. 28

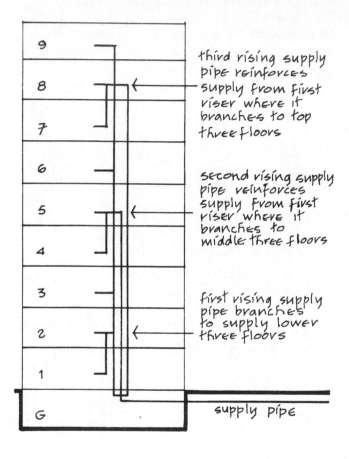

third rising supply pipe reinforces supply from first riser where it branches to top three floors

second rising supply pipe reinforces supply from first riser where it branches to middle three floors

first rising supply pipe branches to supply lower three floors

supply pipe

Fig. 27

There are two mains pressure supply pipes to the lower five floors in the building illustrated in Fig. 28, and the five upper floors are supplied by two rising supply pipes under the pressure of the pump in the basement. The incoming supply pipe is connected to the pump through a check valve assembly.

The auto-pneumatic pressure vessel illustrated in Fig. 29 is a sealed cylinder in which air in the upper part of the cylinder is under pressure from the water pumped into the lower part of the cylinder. The

cushion of air under pressure serves to force water up the supply pipe to feed upper-level outlets as illustrated. Water is drawn from the auto-pneumatic pressure vessel as water is drawn from the upper-level outlets so that when the water level in the pressure vessel falls to a predetermined level the float switch operates the pump to recharge the pressure vessel with water. Thus the cushion of air in the pressure vessel and its float switch control and limit the number of pump operations. In time, air inside the pressure vessel becomes mixed with the water and it is replaced automatically by the air compressor.

Where a gravity fed supply to all fittings other than drinking water outlets is acceptable which has been the common practice in England, then a roof level storage cistern is used.

26

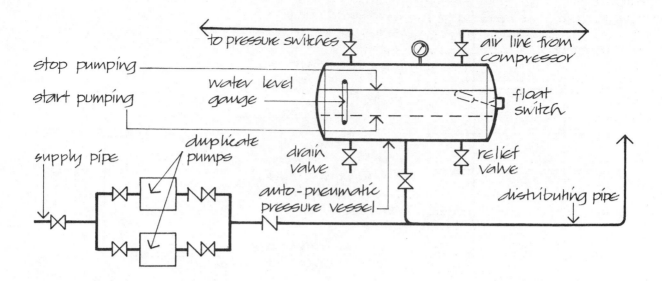

stop pumping

start pumping

to pressure switches

air line from compressor

water level gauge

float switch

supply pipe

duplicate pumps

drain valve

relief valve

auto-pneumatic pressure vessel

distributing pipe

Diagram of Auto-pneumatic system.

Fig. 29

Fig. 30 is an illustration of a ten-storey building in which the drinking-water outlets to the five lower floors are supplied directly from the supply pipe and those above from a separate pumped supply. It will be seen that there are duplicate pumps, one duty pump and one standby pump that comes into operation when the duty pump fails. There is a duplication of rising pipework to the five lower floors which is considered a worthwhile outlay in reducing the load and wear on the pumps. The pumped supply feeds both the higher drinking water outlets and the cold-water storage cistern through a drinking-water storage vessel.

The drinking-water storage vessel with its pipeline switch and the float switch to the cold-water storage cistern are installed to limit the pump operations to reduce wear and tear on the pumps. The sealed drinking-water storage vessel provides a reservoir of water on which the drinking-water outlets draw. When the vessel is empty the pipeline switch operates the pump to recharge the drinking-water storage vessel and the cold-water storage cistern. When the level of water in the cold-water storage cistern falls to a predetermined level then its float switch will operate the pump to recharge the cistern and also the drinking-water storage vessel if need be. In this way

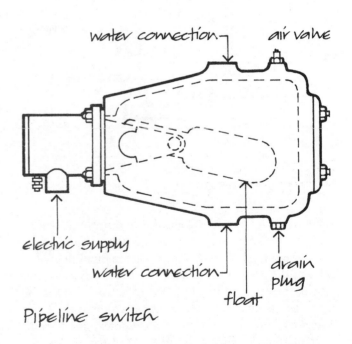

water connection

air valve

electric supply

water connection

float

drain plug

Pipeline switch

Fig. 31

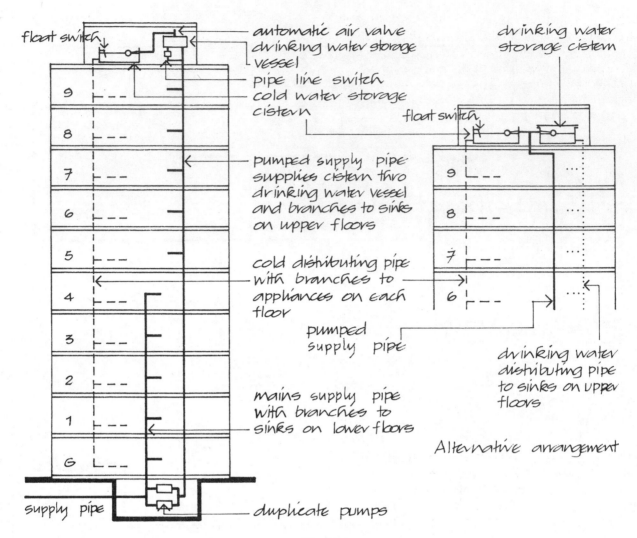

float switch — automatic air valve
drinking water storage vessel
pipe line switch
cold water storage cistern

drinking water storage cistern

float switch

pumped supply pipe supplies cistern thro drinking water vessel and branches to sinks on upper floors

cold distributing pipe with branches to appliances on each floor

pumped supply pipe

mains supply pipe with branches to sinks on lower floors

drinking water distributing pipe to sinks on upper floors

Alternative arrangement

supply pipe — duplicate pumps

Fig. 30

the two switches serve to minimise pump operations and so reduce wear and maintenance. From Fig. 31 it will be seen that the float inside the pipeline switch falls and operates the switch as the drinking-water storage vessel empties. The float illustrated in Fig. 30 operates its switch as the level of water in the cold-water storage cistern falls to a predetermined level.

Instead of a sealed drinking-water storage vessel a drinking-water storage cistern may be used, as illustrated in Fig. 30. The cistern has a sealed cover and filtered air vent and overflow to exclude dirt and dust as illustrated in Fig. 32. A pump cut out, or float switch, controls the pump operations at a predetermined level. As before, a float switch controls pump

operations to fill the cold-water storage cistern. The pumped service pipe feeds both cisterns so that whichever switch operates, then the pump operates to fill both cisterns.

The advantage of the sealed drinking-water storage vessel is that it requires less maintenance than the drinking-water cistern whose ball valve and filters require periodic maintenance.

The roof level switches illustrated in Fig. 30 have to be wired through a control box down to the basement level pumps and the switches will require regular maintenance in a position difficult of access.

As a check to the possibility of backflow from a pumped supply into the main it has been practice to use a low level cistern as feed to the pumped supply to a roof level cistern, so that the air gap between the inlet and the water level in the cistern acts as a check to possible contamination of the mains supply.

It will be seen from Fig. 33 that the drinking outlets to the lower floors are connected to the supply pipe which in turn feeds a low-level storage cistern from which a supply is pumped to the upper-level drinking-water outlets and the roof-level storage cistern. Pump operations are limited by an auto-

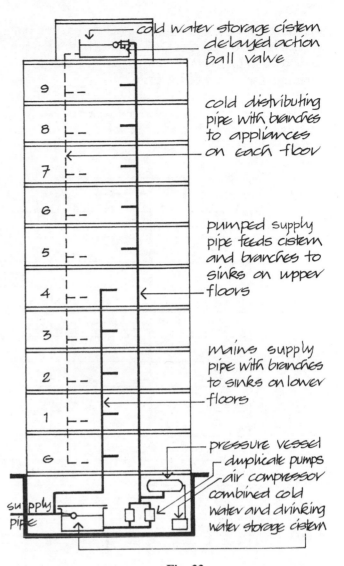

Fig. 33

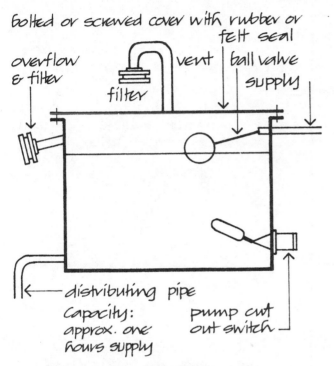

Drinking water storage cistern

Fig. 32

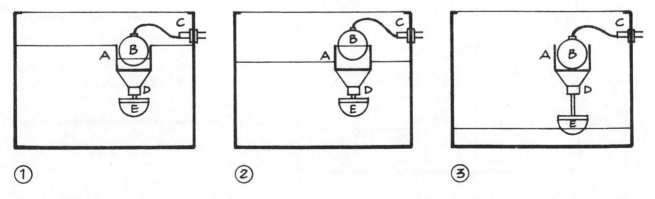

Delayed action Ball valve

Fig. 34

pneumatic pressure vessel and a delayed-action ball valve. As the low-level cistern supplies both drinking and cold-water outlets it has to be airtight to maintain the purity of the drinking supply.

The pumped supply pipe shown in Fig. 33 feeds the roof-level cold-water storage cistern which is fitted with a delayed-action ball valve. The delayed-action ball valve is a mechanical device to limit the number of pump operations. A delayed-action ball valve, illustrated diagrammatically in Fig. 34, consists of a metal cylinder A which fills with water when the cistern is full and in which a ball B floats to operate the valve C to shut off the supply. Water is drawn from the cistern and as the level of water in the cistern falls to a predetermined level, float E falls and opens valve D to discharge the water from cylinder A.

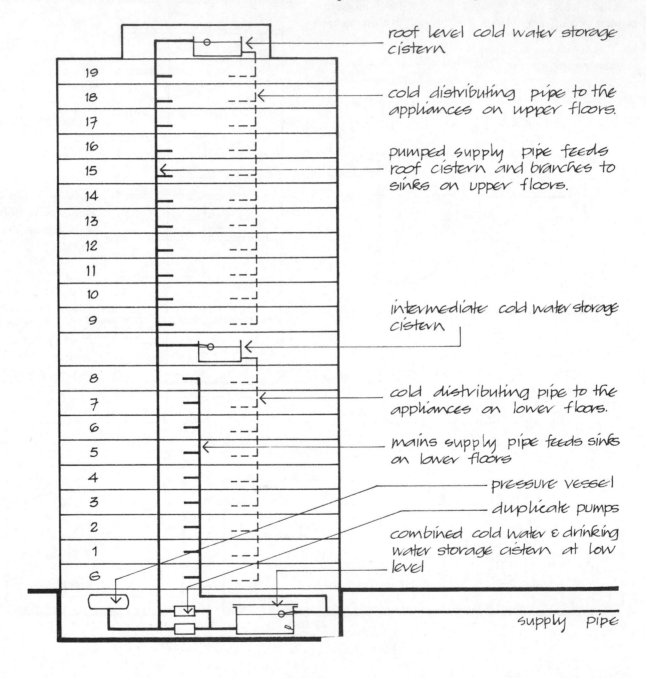

roof level cold water storage cistern

cold distributing pipe to the appliances on upper floors.

pumped supply pipe feeds roof cistern and branches to sinks on upper floors.

intermediate cold water storage cistern

cold distributing pipe to the appliances on lower floors.

mains supply pipe feeds sinks on lower floors

pressure vessel

duplicate pumps

combined cold water & drinking water storage cistern at low level

supply pipe

Fig. 35

The ball *B* falls and opens valve *C* to refill the cistern through the pump so limiting the number of pump operations.

Current practice in multi-storey buildings of more than about ten storeys is to use a roof level and one or more intermediate water storage cisterns to supply outlets other than drinking water taps. The intermediate cisterns spread the very considerable load of water storage and also serve to reduce the pressure in distributing pipes, for which reason they are sometimes termed 'break pressure cisterns'.

It will be seen from Fig. 35 that a ground-level

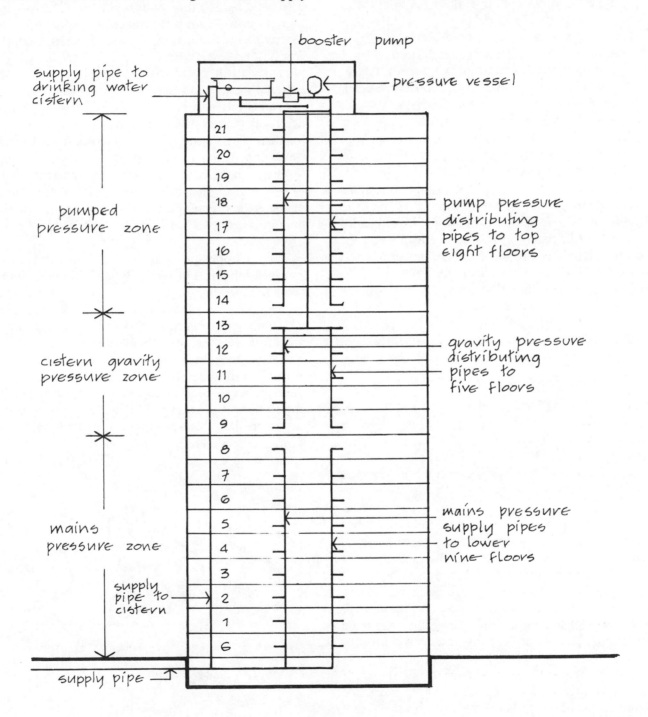

Fig. 36

storage cistern supplies a pumped supply to an intermediate and a roof-level cistern from which distributing pipes supply sanitary appliances to the lower and upper floors respectively thus spreading the weight of water storage and limiting pressure in distributing pipes. The pumped supply also feeds drinking water outlets to upper floors. A float switch in the pressure vessel and delayed-action ball valves in the cisterns limit pump operations. Intermediate cisterns are used at about every tenth floor.

The supply to the twenty-two storey building illustrated in Fig. 36 is divided into three zones. The purpose of the three zones of supply is towards equalisation of pressure and uniformity of flow from outlets on all floors. The supply to the lower nine floors is through two rising supply pipes taken directly from the mains supply. The supply to the eight top floors is from a pumped supply through a roof level pump and pressure vessel and the supply to the intermediate five floors is by gravity from a sealed drinking water cistern at roof level. In this way the loss of residual head to the lower and upper floors is limited and the loss of head from the cistern is limited by feeding intermediate floors only. By dividing the building into three zones of supply, loss of head is limited in the main supply and distribution pipes and by reduction in pipe diameter in each zone, reasonable equalisation of flow from taps on each floor is possible.

PIPES FOR WATER SUPPLY

The materials used for pipework for water supplies are copper, galvanised mild steel and plastic.

Up to the middle of this century lead was the material most used for water-supply pipework. The increase in the cost of lead after the Second World War led first to the use of galvanised mild steel tubes and later to light-gauge copper tubes instead of lead. Today, light-gauge copper tube is the material most used for water-supply pipework in buildings.

Minute quantities of lead may be leached from lead pipes used for water supplies. These small amounts of lead may in time be sufficiently toxic particularly to the young, to be a serious hazard to health.

The new Water Supply Byelaws prohibit the use of lead for either new or replacement pipework for water supply. The Byelaws also prohibit the use of lead solders for jointing copper pipes and in lieu of them, tin/silver solders are accepted.

Copper pipe (copper tubulars): The comparatively high strength of copper facilitates the use of thin-walled light-gauge pipes or tubes for most hot- and cold-water services. The ductility of copper facilitates cold bending, the thin walls make for a light-weight material and the smooth surface of the pipe provides low resistance to the flow of water. Like lead, copper oxidises on exposure to air and the oxide film prevents further corrosion. Copper tube is the material most used for water services today.

Copper tubes are supplied as half-hard temper and dead soft temper, the former for use above ground for their rigidity and the latter principally for use in trenches or where their flexibility is an advantage as for use as the underground service pipe to buildings. Light-gauge copper tube, size 6 to 159 mm (outside diameter) is manufactured – the sizes most used in buildings being – 15, 18, 22, 28, 35, 42 and 54mm.

Jointing: Copper pipes are joined with capillary or compression joints or by welding, the first two joints being used for the majority of copper tubes used for water services and the latter for the larger bore pipe for drains above ground where the pipework is prefabricated in the plumbers' shop.

A capillary joint is made by fitting plain ends of pipe into a shouldered brass socket. Molten solder is then run into the joint or internal solder is melted by application of heat, Fig. 37 illustrates typical capillary joints. It will be seen that this is a compact, neat joint. Pipe ends and fittings must be clean, else the solder will not adhere firmly to the pipe and socket.

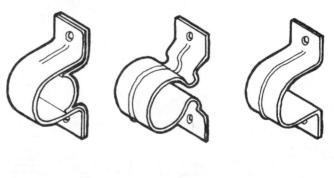

Copper fixing clips

Fig. 38

Compression fittings are either non-manipulative or manipulative. With the former plain pipe ends are gripped by pressure from shaped copper rings and in the latter the ends of the pipes are shaped to the fitting as illustrated in Fig. 37. The manipulative fitting is used for long pipe runs and where pipework is not readily accessible, as the shaped pipe ends are more firmly secured than with the non-manipulative or capillary joint. The somewhat more expensive non-manipulative joint is sometimes preferred to the cheaper capillary joint which is dependent on cleanliness of contact rather than friction.

Copper pipework should be secured with clips at intervals of from 1.5 to 3.0 m horizontally and 2.0 to 3.0 m vertically as illustrated in Fig. 38.

Galvanised mild steel tubulars (pipe): Galvanised mild steel tubulars were commonly used for all water services during the middle of this century because of the low cost and availability of the material. Today,

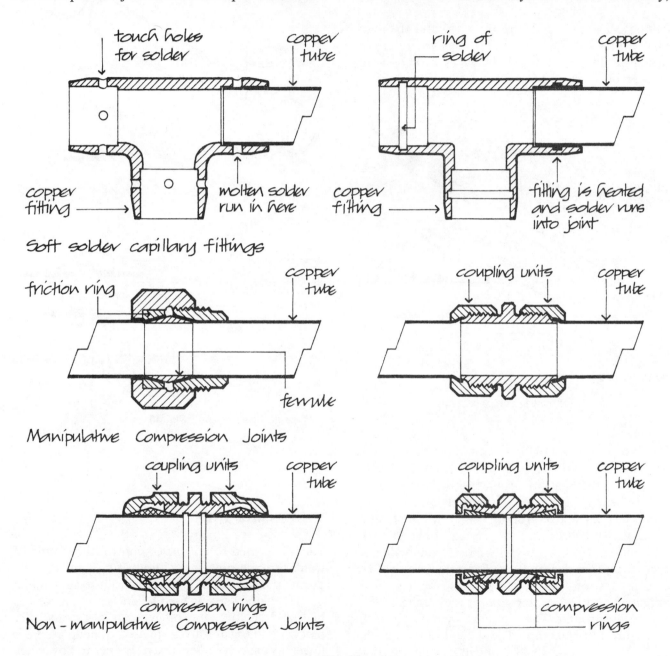

Fig. 37

mild steel tubulars are used for service pipes where the strength of the material and its resistance to high pressures is an advantage. Galvanised mild steel tubulars are manufactured with a nominal bore of 6 to 150 mm in three grades; Light, banded brown; Medium, banded blue; and Heavy, banded red. In general, Light is for gas services, Medium for water services and Heavy for steam pressure services. For water services tubulars should be galvanised to resist corrosion.

Jointing: The pipe ends are threaded and the joint made with sockets, nipples or long screws, unions or fittings as illustrated in Fig. 39. Pipes are supported at intervals of from 2.5 to 3.0 metres.

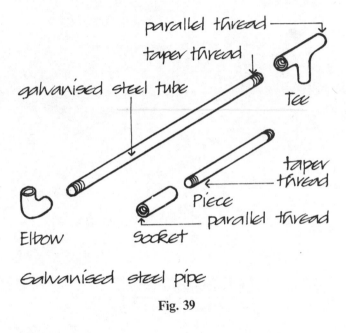

Fig. 39

Plastic pipe or tube: Polythene and unplasticised PVC (Poly Vinyl Chloride) tube is used respectively for use underground and above ground for water services.

Polythene (Polyethylene) is flexible and used for water services under ground while the more rigid unplasticised PVC is used for services above ground. Both materials are lightweight, cheap, tough, do not corrode and are easily joined. These materials soften at comparatively low temperatures and are used principally for cold-water services and drains above and below ground. The pipes are manufactured in sizes from 17 to 609 mm. The sizes most used being 21.2, 26.6, 33.4, 42.1, 48.1 and 60.2 mm (outside diameter).

Jointing: Polythene tube is jointed with compression fittings as illustrated in Fig. 40 and PVC with a solvent-welded joint as illustrated in Fig. 40. Pipe runs are fixed at intervals of 225 to 500 mm horizontally and 350 to 900 mm vertically.

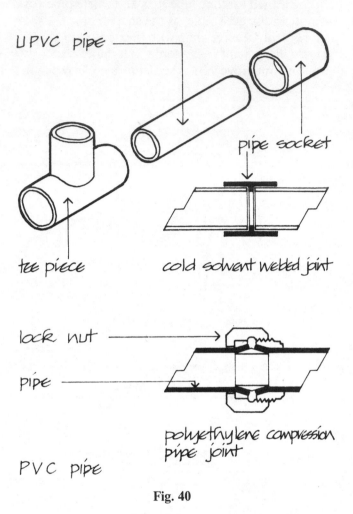

Fig. 40

VALVES AND TAPS

Valves are used to cut off or control the supply of water through pipework. The two types of valve in use are the globe and the gate valve illustrated in Fig. 41. The globe valve is used where water pressure is high and positive shut off is essential as in service pipework and gate valves are used where pressure is lower, as the valve offers less resistance to flow when open.

34

Taps control the supply of hot and cold water to sanitary appliances. There may be separate hot and cold taps to each sanitary appliance or combined hot and cold taps with a common outlet.

The Water Supply Byelaws will require an air gap between the lowest part of the outlet of water taps and the spill over level of sanitary appliances such as baths, basins and sinks to prevent contamination of mains supplies by backsiphonage, backflow or cross connection. The air gap is related to the bore of the pipe supplying the tap or the bore of the outlet as set out in Table 1. Fig. 42 is an illustration of a tap designed to match this requirement. As an alternative to an air gap a double check valve assembly or other suitable appliance may be used in the pipe supplying each tap.

Individual taps are generally of the screw-down valve type, the most used being the bib tap and the pillar tap illustrated in Fig. 43. The bib tap is for fixing on the wall over a sanitary appliance, and the pillar tap for fixing to holes in the sanitary appliance.

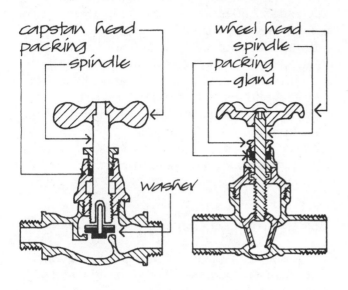

Globe valve   Gate or sluice valve

Fig. 41

Table 1. Air gap

Bore of pipe or outlet	Vertical distance between point of outlet and spill-over level
(1) not exceeding 14mm	20mm
(2) exceeding 14mm but not exceeding 21mm	25mm
(3) exceeding 21mm but not exceeding 41mm	70mm
(4) exceeding 41mm	twice the bore of the outlet.

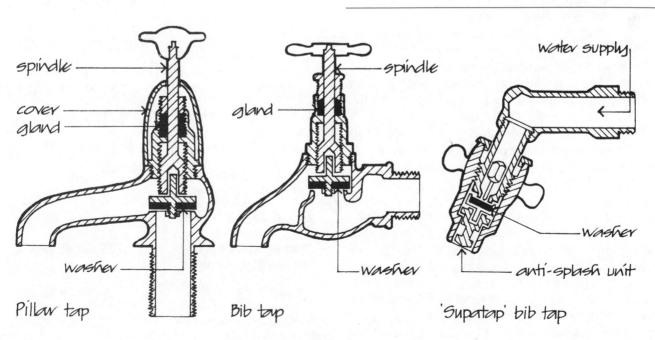

Pillar tap   Bib tap   'Supatap' bib tap

Fig. 43

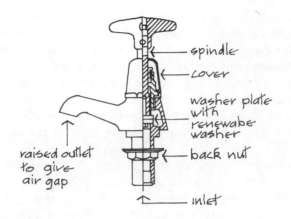

Tap with raised outlet

Fig. 42

Bib taps are alike in design. The various pillar taps available are designed for appearance rather than utilitarian purposes.

A wide range of combined hot and cold taps with a common outlet is available, some with individual taps and others with a single control to mix the hot and cold water through a valve. These mixing valves are used for showers to avoid the discharge of scalding hot water.

Spring-loaded percussion taps are often used for washbasins in public toilets. The taps are operated by a spring-loaded push which returns to the off position once the push is released to avoid the likelihood of the tap being left running.

Spray taps discharge a fine spray cone of water sufficient for hand washing and are used in public and communal toilets. Appreciable economy in the use of water is effected by the use of these taps.

The 'supatap', illustrated in Fig. 43, is designed so that the washer may be replaced without turning off the water supply through a check valve that interrupts the supply.

Insulation: Cold and hot water supply and distributing pipes should be fixed inside buildings, preferably away from external walls to avoid the possibility of water freezing, expanding and rupturing pipes and joints. Where pipes are run inside rooftop tank rooms and in unheated roof spaces, they should be insulated with one of the wrap around, or sectional insulation materials designed for the purpose. Similarly, roof-level and roof-space storage cisterns

should be fitted with an insulation lining to all sides, the base, and to the top of the cisterns.

WATER STORAGE CAPACITY AND PIPE SIZES

In areas where Water Board regulations have required cold-water storage, the Byelaws required an actual storage capacity of 114 litres for cold supply only and 227 litres where the cistern supplied cold and domestic hot water.

British Standard 6700, 1987 recommends minimum storage for dwellings of 100 to 150 litres for small houses, for cold water only, and 100 litres per bedroom, total capacity, for larger houses.

Water-storage capacity was determined by the regulations of water undertakings for dwellings at 114 and 227 litres for cold and domestic hot water respectively and for other uses from Table 2.

Table 2. Cold water storage

Recommended minimum storage of cold water for domestic purposes (hot and cold outlets)	
Type of building or occupation	**Minimum storage litres**
Hostel	90 per bedspace
Hotel	200 per bedspace
Office premises with canteen facilities without canteen facilities	45 per employee 40 per employee
Restaurant	7 per meal
Day school nursery primary	15 per pupil
secondary technical	20 per pupil
Boarding school	90 per pupil
Children's home or residential nursery	135 per bedspace
Nurses' home	120 per bedspace
Nursing or convalescent home	135 per bedspace

Estimation of pipe sizes: To provide a reasonable rate of flow from outlets, that is taps and valves, the required size of pipe depends on the static or pumped head of water pressure, the resistance to flow of the pipes, fittings and bends and the assumed frequency of use of outlets. For small pipe installations such as the average dwelling where there are 5 to 10 outlets, pipes of sufficient bore are used to allow simultaneous use of all outlets at peak use times. As only small bore pipes are required for this maximum rate of flow it is idle to make an estimate of pipe size for a more realistic condition. With larger installations, such as the pipe system for a block of flats, where there may be 100 or more outlets, it would be unrealistic and uneconomic in pipe size and cost to assume that all outlets will be in use simultaneously. It is usual therefore to make an assumption of the frequency of use of outlets, to estimate required pipe sizes to give a reasonable rate of flow from outlets that it is assumed will be in use simultaneously at peak use times. If the actual simultaneous use is greater than the estimate then there will be reduced rate of flow from outlets. This 'failure' of the pipe system to meet actual in-use flow rates has to be accepted in any estimate of frequency of use of outlets.

The rate of water flow at taps and outlets depends on the diameter of the outlet and the pressure of water at the tap or outlet. The size of the tap is fixed. The water pressure depends on the source water pressure from a cold water storage cistern or a pumped supply and the loss of pressure to the frictional resistance of the pipework and its fittings such as elbows, tees, valves and taps. The design of pipework installation is concerned, therefore, in estimating the resistance to flow and the selection of pipes of sufficient size to allow a reasonable rate of flow at taps, where the source water pressure is known.

In the design of pipework for buildings it is convenient to express water pressure as hydraulic or static head, which is proportional to pressure. The static head is the vertical distance in metres between the source, the cold water storage cistern and the tap or outlet. This head represents the pressure or energy available to provide a flow of water from outlets against the frictional resistance of the pipework and its fittings. The frictional resistance to flow of pipes is expressed as loss of head (pressure) for unit length of pipe. These loss of head values are tabulated against the various pipe diameters available and the various materials in use. The frictional resistance to flow of fittings such as elbows, tees, valves and taps is large in comparison to their length in the pipe run. To simplify calculation it is usual to express the frictional resistance of fittings as a length of pipe whose resistance to flow is equivalent to that of the fitting. Thus the resistance to flow of a tee is given as an equivalent pipe length. In Table 3 the equivalent length of pipe is given. From this the frictional resistance of a pipe and its fittings can be expressed as an equivalent length of pipe, that is the actual length plus an equivalent length for the resistance of the fittings. The head (pressure) in that pipe can then be distributed along the equivalent length of pipe to give a permissible rate of loss of head per metre run of equivalent pipe length, and the head remaining at any point along the pipe determined. From this, the pipe diameter required for a given rate of flow in pipework and at outlets can be calculated.

To select the required pipe sizes in an installation it is often useful to prepare an orthographic or isometric diagram of the pipe runs from the scale drawings of the building. This diagram need not be to scale as the pipe lengths and head available will in any event be scaled off the drawings of the building. The purpose of the diagram is for clarity in selecting pipe sizes and tabulating these calculations. The more extensive the installation the more useful the diagram will be.

Fig. 44 is an isometric diagram of a cold distribution pipe installation, not to scale. The source of supply, the cold water storage cistern is shown. The head from the base of the cistern is dimensioned and all pipe runs to sanitary appliances are indicated. Each pipe run is numbered between tees and tees and tees and taps. A change of pipe diameter is most

Table 3. Equivalent pipelengths

Pipe fittings	Equivalent length of pipe in pipe diameters
90° Elbows	30
Tees	40
Gate valve	20
Globe valves and taps	300

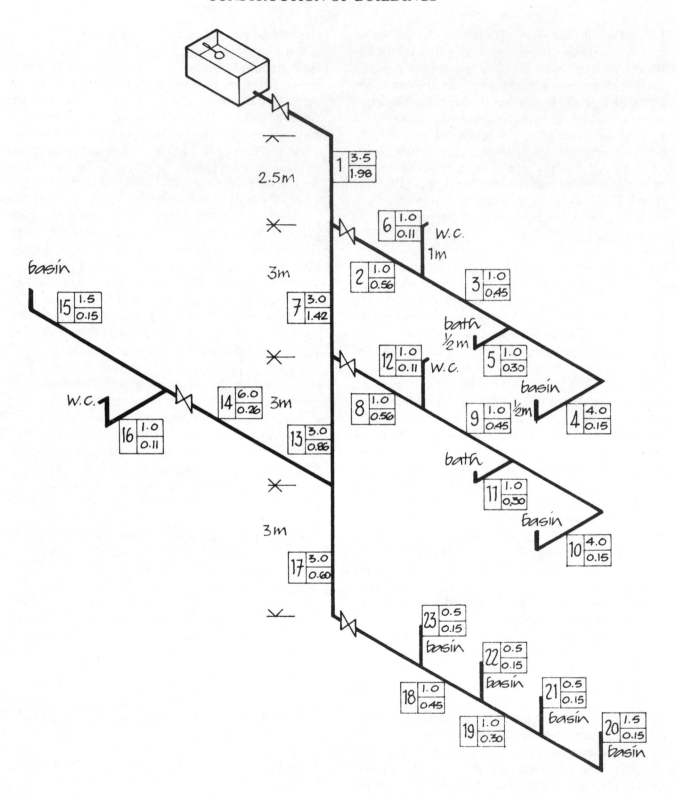

Fig. 44

likely to be required at tees and it is convenient, therefore, to number pipes between these points and taps. There are various methods of numbering pipe runs. The method adopted in the diagram is a box, one corner of which points to the pipe or one side of which is along the pipe run. The box contains the pipe number on the left hand side and the actual pipe length top right and the rate of flow in litres per second bottom right. The rate of flow in a pipe is the rate of flow of the single sanitary appliance it serves or the accumulation of all the rates of flow of all the sanitary appliances it serves. In Fig. 44 the head is measured from the base of the cistern to the taps or pipe runs. Some measure from midway between the water line and the base of the cistern and others from some short distance below the cistern to allow a safety margin and to allow for furring of pipes. For most building installations it is usual to take head measurements from the base of the cistern.

In the following calculations to determine pipe sizes it is assumed that it is possible that all the taps served may be open simultaneously and the pipes are sized accordingly. In large installations such as those to multi-storey blocks of flats it is unlikely that all taps will be open at the same time and a frequency of use assumption, described later, is made to avoid the expense of over-large pipes.

The procedure for selecting pipe sizes is to determine the first index or critical run of pipes. The first index run of pipes is that along which taps are most likely to be starved of water when all the taps are open. This starvation or loss of rate of flow is most likely to occur in the branch closest to the cistern where head is least. The first index run in Fig. 44 is pipe run 1, 2, 3 and 4. If pipes of adequate size for this run are selected to provide the required rates of flow at taps then pipe run 1 will be large enough to supply all the other taps to the rest of the installation.

The head of water available in the first index run 1, 2, 3 and 4 is 2 m, the vertical distance from the base of the cistern to the tap of the wash basin. The rate of flow from taps determines the cumulative rate of flow in the pipe runs. The unknown factors are the frictional resistance of the pipework and fittings and the size of pipes required for the given rates of flow. It is necessary, therefore, to make an initial assumption of one of these unknowns — the pipe sizes.

To make this initial assumption it is necessary to calculate a rate of loss of head in the index pipe run. The actual length of the pipes is known and it is necessary to make an estimate of the likely length of pipe whose resistance to flow is equivalent to the resistance of the pipe fittings. This is usually taken as a percentage of the actual pipe length. The percentage may vary from 25 to over 100. With experience in pipe sizing this assumed percentage will approach a fair degree of accuracy. In general the greater the number of fittings to each unit length of pipe the higher the percentage.

In Fig. 44 pipe run 1, 2, 3 and 4 has an actual length of 9.5 m. Assume an equivalent length of about 50% or say 5.5 m. Thus the total equivalent length of pipe is $9.5 + 5.5 = 15$ m. The head is 2 m. The permissible rate of loss of head is therefore $2/15 = 0.13$ per metre of equivalent length of pipe and this rate of loss of head should not be exceeded at any point along the pipe run.

The graph in Fig. 45 is used to select pipe sizes where the rate of flow is known and rate of loss of head has been assumed. The rate of loss of head is 0.13. From that figure on the base line read up to 1.98 litres per second, the flow required in pipe 1. These two intersect roughly midway between the heavy oblique lines indicating 35 and 42 mm pipe sizes. If the 35 mm pipe were selected then the rate of loss of head would be greater than the permissible loss of head figure of 0.13 so the next larger size, 42 mm is selected for pipe run 1. Similarly for pipe runs 2, 3 and 4 from the 0.13 rate of loss of head on the graph read up to 0.56, 0.45 and 0.15 rates of flow to select pipe sizes 28, 28 and 18 mm respectively, choosing as before the pipe size above the intersection of points.

These assumed pipe sizes will now be used to make a more exact calculation of friction losses in pipes and fittings and a more exact selection of pipe sizes. For this purpose it is usual to tabulate the calculations 95 set out in Fig. 46.

The pipe numbers, design flow rates and actual pipe lengths of pipe runs 1, 2, 3 and 4, the first index run, are entered in columns, 1, 2 and 3 and the assumed diameters in column 7.

The friction losses for each pipe run due to elbows, tees, valves and taps are now calculated. These may be determined by a multiplier of the assumed pipe diameters to give an equivalent length of pipe from Table 3 or more accurately from tables published by the Chartered Institution of Building Services Engineers.

In pipe run 1 there is a gate valve, an elbow and a tee, the figures for which from Table 3 are 20, 30 and

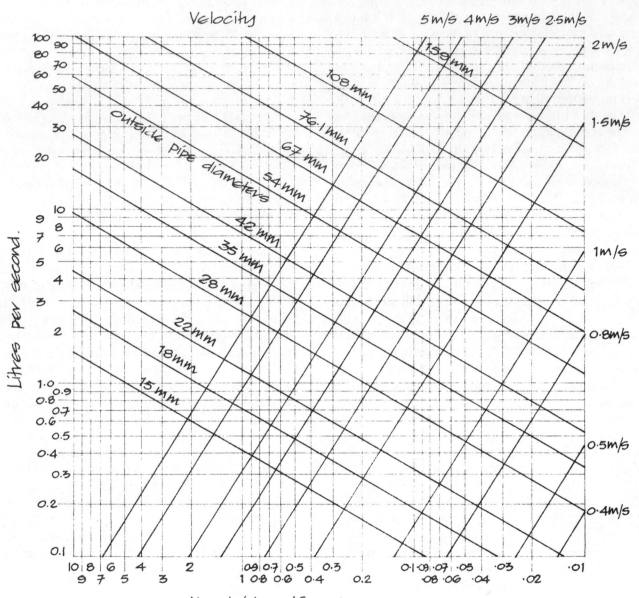

Graph for selection of copper pipe sizes
Pipe sizes are outside diameters.

Fig. 45

Table of assumptions and calculations for pipe sizes

1	2	3	4	5	6	7	8	9	10	11	12
Pipe No.	Design flow	Length	Equiv. Length	Total Eq. length	Head available	Assumed diam.	Permissible H/L value	Actual H/L value	Head used	Head remaining	Final diam.
1	1.98	3.5	3.8	7.3	2.0	42	0.09	0.085	0.62	1.38	42
2	0.56	1.0	1.7	2.7	1.38	28	0.09	0.06	0.16	1.22	28
3	0.45	1.0	1.1	2.1	1.22	28	0.09	0.04	0.08	1.14	28
4	0.15	4.0	6.5	10.5	1.14	18	0.09	0.06	0.63	0.51	18
5	0.30	1.0	6.0	7.0	1.14	18	0.16	0.08			22
6	0.11	1.0	5.0	6.0	0.72	15	0.12	0.09			15
7	1.42	3.0	1.4	4.4	4.88	35	1.1	0.35	1.54	3.34	28
8	0.56	1.0			3.34						
9	0.45										
10	0.15										
11											

Fig. 46

40 respectively. The sum of these, 90, multiplied by the assumed pipe diameter of 42 give an equivalent pipe length of 90 × 42 or 3.8 m. Thus the total of actual length of pipe 1, and equivalent length for fittings is 3.5 + 3.8 = 7.3 m and this figure is entered in column 5. Similarly for pipe run 2 there is a valve and a tee, 20 + 40 = 60 which multiplied by the assumed pipe diameter of 28 gives an equivalent length of 1.68, say 1.7 which is entered in column 4 to give a total length of 2.7 in column 5. For pipe run 3 there is one tee, 40, which gives an equivalent length of 40 × 28 = 1.12, say 1.1. In pipe run 4 there are two elbows 30 + 30 and one tap, 300 a total of 360 which multiplied by the assumed pipe diameter of 18 equals 6.48, say 6.5 to give a total equivalent length of 10.5.

With these more accurate totals of equivalent lengths in column 5 it is now possible to make a more accurate calculation of rate of loss of head. The head is 2 m and the total of equivalent lengths in column 5 is 22.6. Thus the permissible rate of loss of head is $^2/_{22.6} = 0.09$ which is entered in column 8. With this more accurate rate of loss of head value final pipe sizes are selected from Fig. 45. For pipe run 1 the head loss and flow lines intersect just below the 42 mm pipe size line confirming the assumed pipe size. The 42 mm pipe size line intersects the 1.98 flow line

above a head loss value of 0.085 so that the actual head loss value in selecting the 42 mm pipe will be less than the permissible head loss value. The actual head loss in pipe run 1 will, therefore, be 0.085 which multiplied by the total equivalent length of 7.3, which is 0.62 and this figure is entered in column 10 to give a figure of 1.38 head remaining in column 11. This figure of 1.38, head remaining at the end of pipe 1 will therefore be the head available for pipe 2 and this figure is entered in column 6 for pipe 2. Similarly this head remaining at the end of pipe 1 will also be available for pipe 7.

Similarly for pipe runs 2, 3 and 4, taking the permissible head loss value of 0.09 from Fig. 45, the required pipe sizes are 28, 28 and 18 mm respectively and the actual *rate* of head losses 0.06, 0.04 and 0.06. From these figures the head used and head remaining are calculated and tabulated. To calculate pipe sizes for pipe runs 5 and 6, tabulate pipe numbers, design flow and actual length. Assume pipe diameters of say 18 and 15 mm respectively, as these are common pipe sizes for branches to baths and W.C.s, then calculate equivalent lengths for fittings as before, based on these assumed pipe sizes, then tabulate total equivalent lengths. The head available for pipe 5 is taken from Fig. 46 as the head remaining at the end of pipe run 3, that is 1.14. From the head available and the total equivalent length a permissible head loss value of 0.16 is calculated and a pipe size of 22 mm is taken from Fig. 45. The head available for pipe run 6 is the head remaining at the end of pipe run 2, that is 1.22, less half a metre, the height of the top of pipe run 6 above that of pipe run 4. The head available is therefore 0.72, the permissible head loss value is 0.12 and the pipe size is 15 mm.

To determine the pipe size for pipe run 7 tabulate in columns 1, 2 and 3 as before. Now assume a pipe size for pipe run 7. As the flow in 7 is less than in pipe 1 and the head will be greater, assume that pipe run 7 will be the next size smaller than 1, that is 35 mm. On this assumption calculate equivalent length for fittings of 1.4 and total equivalent length of 4.4. The head available at the junction of pipe runs 1 and 7 is the head at that point which is 2.5 less the head used in pipe 1, which from Fig. 46, column 10 is 0.62, so that the head available at the junction of pipes 1 and 7 is 2.5 − 0.62 which is 1.88. The head along the length of pipe 7 is 3.0 so the head available in pipe run 7 is 1.88 + 3.0 or 4.88. The permissible head loss value is the head available divided by the total equivalent length, that is $\frac{4.88}{4.4} = 1.1$. From Fig. 45 for a rate of flow of 1.42 and a permissible head loss value of 1.1 a 28 mm pipe is selected. The actual head loss is then as before and the head used and head remaining calculated and tabulated. This head remaining will be tabulated as available for pipe run 8. The procedure outlined above is used in selecting pipe sizes for the rest of the pipe installation.

The table is a record which can be used to check the calculations leading to the selection of pipe sizes, to confirm that actual head losses do not exceed the permissible head losses and, therefore, that pressure is available to provide the required rates of flow at taps and as a basis for subsequent calculations required by any change of plans.

In the example of selection of pipe sizes for the installation shown in Fig. 44, it was assumed that there was a possibility that all the taps might be open at the same time and pipe sizes were selected against this possibility. For small pipe installations such as those for houses and other small buildings and for branches from main pipe runs in large installations it is usual to assume pipe sizes sufficient for simultaneous use of all taps. In these situations only small pipe diameters will be required and no appreciable economic advantage in a reduction of pipe sizes would

be obtained by making another assumption.

In extensive pipe installations it is usual to assume a frequency of use figure for the taps to sanitary appliances so that smaller pipe sizes may be used than would be were it assumed that all taps were open simultaneously. Frequency-of-use values for individual sanitary appliances are expressed as loading or demand units as set out in Table 4, the accumulation of these units for sanitary appliances being used to determine notional rates of flow in pipes. In Fig. 44 the loading units of all the sanitary appliances taken from Table 4 are 3 W.C.s, $3 \times 2 = 6$, 7 basins, $7 \times 1\frac{1}{2} = 10\frac{1}{2}$ and 2 baths, $2 \times 10 = 20$, a total of $36\frac{1}{2}$ loading units. This total of loading units would require a rate of flow of 0.68 litres/sec., in pipe run 1. Applying this figure to Fig. 45, with a permissible head loss figure of 0.09 in pipe run 1, a pipe size of 28 mm would be selected — as compared to the 42 mm pipe based on an assumption of simultaneous use of all taps. If the same loading units are then applied to the pipe run 2, 3 and 4 the sum total of the units is so small as to make no significant difference in the selection of pipe sizes and the sizes previously selected will be used. From this example it will be seen that the use of loading units to determine rates of flow in pipes makes no significant economy in the selection of pipe sizes in pipe runs that serve a few sanitary appliances. As a general rule where pipe runs serve fewer than say ten sanitary appliances it is not worth while using loading units to economise in pipe sizes.

Table 4. Loading units

Appliances	Loading units
WC flushing cistern (9L)	2
Wash basin	1½ to 3
Bath tap of nom. size ¾	10
Bath tap of nom. size 1	22
Shower	3
Sink tap of nom. size ½	3
Sink tap of nom. size ¾	5

CHAPTER TWO

SANITARY APPLIANCES

Sanitary appliances, sometimes termed sanitary fittings, include all fixed appliances in which water is used either for flushing foul matter away or in which water is used for cleaning, culinary and drinking purposes. The former, termed soil appliances, include W.C.s and urinals the discharge from which is described as soil water and the latter, termed waste appliances, include wash-basins, baths, showers, sinks and bidets the discharge from which is described as waste water.

SOIL APPLIANCES

W.C. suite: A W.C. suite comprises a W.C. pan, seat, flushing appliance and any necessary flush pipe.

The W.C. pan is a ceramic or metal bowl to take solid and liquid excrement, with an inlet for flushing and a trapped outlet. The seat is usually a plastic ring secured to the back of the pan. The usual flushing appliance is a cistern designed to discharge water rapidly into the pan through a flush pipe for cleaning and disposal of contents. The flushing cistern may be fixed high above, near to or close coupled to the pan, the three arrangements being described as high-level, low-level (low-down) or close-coupled W.C. suites as illustrated in Fig. 47.

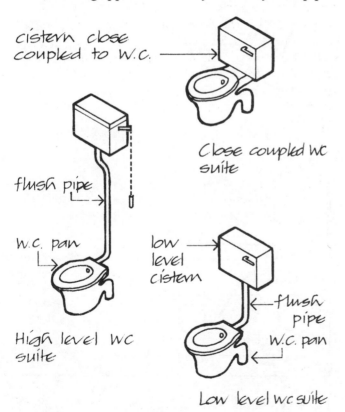

Fig. 47

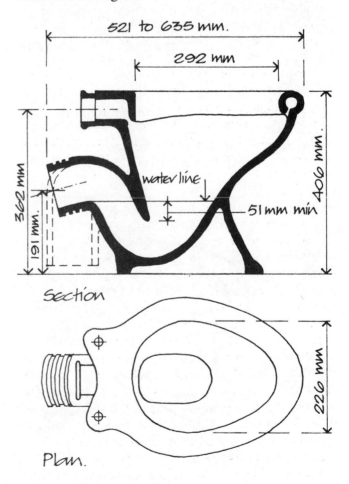

Fig. 48

43

The high-level suite is no longer popular because of the long unsightly flush pipe and the noisy operation of the flush. It has the advantage that the force of water from the long flush pipe effectively cleans the pan. The low-level or low-down suite is much used today for its appearance. The flush is less noisy than that of the high-level suite and less effective in cleansing the pan. The close-coupled suite is so called because the flushing cistern is fixed directly above the back of the pan for the sake of appearance. As the flush water does not discharge into the pan with force, it is at once comparatively quiet in operation and less effective in cleansing. A siphonic W.C. pan is often part of a close-coupled suite for the sake of its comparatively quiet operation. Close-coupled suites are more expensive than low-level suites.

W.C. pans: The two types of pan in use today, the washdown and the siphonic, are distinguished by the operation of the flush water in cleansing and discharging the contents of the pan. The flush water discharges into the wash-down pan around the rim to cleanse the sides of the pan and as the bowl fills, the water in the trap overturns to discharge the contents and as the flush continues it refills the trap. Fig. 48 is an illustration of a typical washdown pan. It will be seen that the back of the pan is near vertical and the sides steeply sloping to minimise fouling. The

area of water in the pan should be as large as possible to receive foul matter.

The siphonic pan operates either by part of the flush water entering the air space between two water seals or by the discharge causing siphonic action in the outlet. In the former, part of the flush water enters the air space between the two water seals, causes the lower trap to overturn and the momentary reduction in pressure causes the upper trap to siphon out so discharging the contents. The continuing flush then recharges the two traps. In the latter the flush causes a full bore flow in the outgo, a reduction in pressure and a siphonic discharge of the pan. Again the continuing flush refills the trap. Fig. 49 is an illustration of siphonic W.C. pans.

Most W.C. pans are of the pedestal type, the base or pedestal being made integral with the pan. The

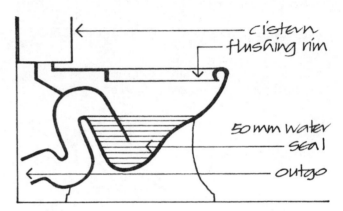

Single seal siphon W.C. pan

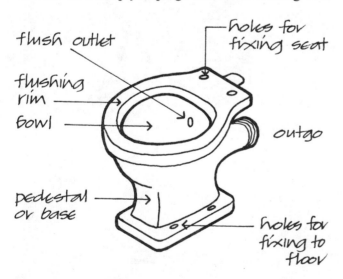

Pedestal W.C. pan

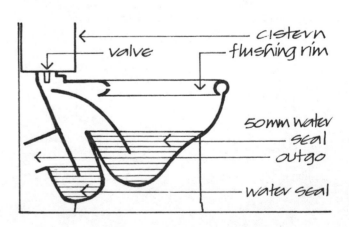

Double seal siphonic W.C. pan

Fig. 50   Fig. 49

pan is secured to the floor with screws through holes in the pedestal base to timber plugs in solid floors or directly to timber floors. Fig. 50 is an illustration of a typical pedestal W.C. pan.

Most W.C. pans are made of vitreous china which, after firing, has an impermeable body and a hard, smooth, glazed finish which is readily cleaned. The flushing cistern body and cover to close-coupled W.C. suites is also made of vitreous china for the sake of appearance. W.C. pans have integral traps to contain a water seal against odours from the drain pipes or drains.

The traditional pan is manufactured with either 'P' or 'S' trap outgoes with either straight, right or left-hand outgoes to suit various arrangements of the pan in relation to the position of the soil pipe. P and S traps are so named for their sectional similarity to the letters. Fig. 51 illustrates typical outgoes to W.C. pans. In specifying this traditional type of pan, it is necessary to nominate either 'P' or 'S' trap outlet and a straight or right hand or left hand outgo.

The current standard W.C. pan has a horizontal outlet, as illustrated in Fig. 52, to which separate outlet pipe fittings are connected for straight, right or left hand outgoes. This arrangement greatly simplifies production, in the manufacture of a single type of pan.

Fig. 53 is an illustration of connections of W.C. pan outgoes to soil branches in cast iron, plastic and copper. Where the W.C. pan is fixed to a timber floor the outgo of the pan should be connected to the soil branch with a flexible joint capable of accommodating movements of the floor as illustrated in Fig. 54. If the pan outgo were connected with a rigid joint there would be a likelihood of the pan outgo cracking.

W.C. seats are moulded from plastic and are generally in the form of a ring seat or a ring seat with a separate cover as illustrated in Fig. 55. The seat or seat and cover are secured to the back of the pan with bolts and pillars so that both the seat and cover hinge to raise vertically. The open front seat and the inset seat illustrated in Fig. 55 are for use in male toilets. The inset seat is little used as it is liable to be fouled and is difficult to keep clean.

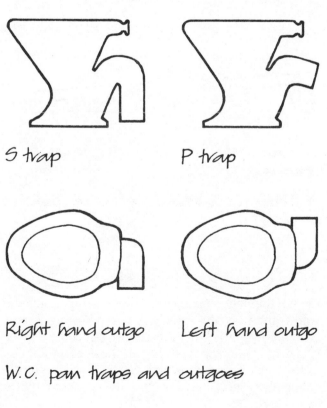

S trap   P trap

Right hand outgo   Left hand outgo

W.C. pan traps and outgoes

Fig. 51

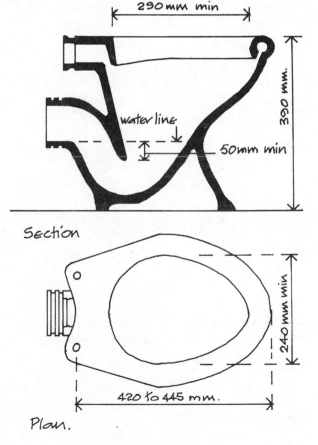

290mm min

390 mm.

water line

50mm min

Section

240 mm min

420 to 445 mm.

Plan.

Fig. 52

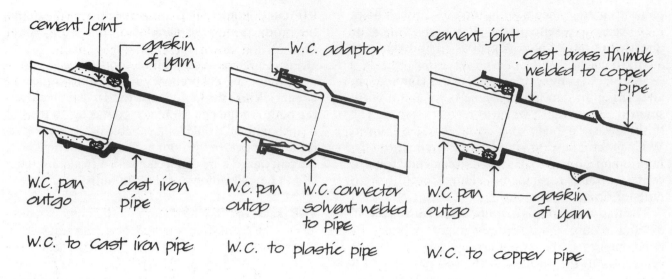

cement joint
gaskin of yarn
W.C. pan outgo
cast iron pipe

W.C. to cast iron pipe

W.C. adaptor
W.C. pan outgo
W.C. connector solvent welded to pipe

W.C. to plastic pipe

cement joint
cast brass thimble welded to copper pipe
W.C. pan outgo
gaskin of yarn

W.C. to copper pipe

Fig. 53

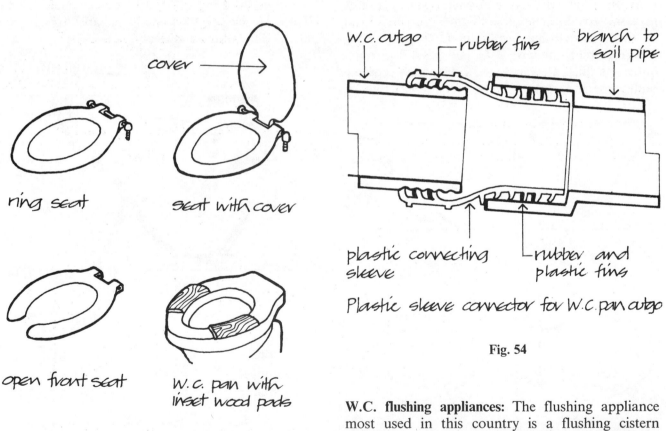

cover

ring seat

seat with cover

open front seat

W.C. pan with inset wood pads

Fig. 55

W.C. outgo
rubber fins
branch to soil pipe
plastic connecting sleeve
rubber and plastic fins

Plastic sleeve connector for W.C. pan outgo

Fig. 54

W.C. flushing appliances: The flushing appliance most used in this country is a flushing cistern containing 9 litres of water and operated by a lever, push or chain. Some water authorities in Europe accept the use of flushing valves that operate to discharge a predetermined volume of water by the operation of a lever or a push. With wear these valves may discharge more water than they were originally designed to discharge and with wear they may drip and waste water. Because of this the water authorities in this country insist on the use of flushing cisterns which used to, until fairly recently, be termed WWPs, water waste preventers.

Fig. 56 is an illustration of typical flushing cisterns. It will be seen that the standard cistern is somewhat bulky. The so-called 'slimline' cisterns are neither so bulky nor obtrusive for appearance sake nor for fixing in a duct behind the pan.

Flushing cisterns discharge water in one operation through a flush pipe or directly to the pan by siphonic action. Fig. 57 is an illustration of a typical flushing cistern. It will be seen that the cistern is filled through a valve operated by a ball float and arm similar to that described for water-storage cisterns.

When the Water Supply Byelaws come into effect early in 1988, it will be a requirement that there be an air gap between the highest level of water in the cistern and the outlet of the float valve. This air gap is related to the bore of the supply pipe and is the same as that for storage cisterns. The requirement for an air gap will prohibit the use of silencer pipes or tubes, such as that shown in Fig. 57.

The plastic siphon is operated by a lever which raises a piston to force water over the siphon bend and the siphonic action causes the water in the cistern to follow, through perforations in the piston, up the siphon and down the flush pipes in one go. A distributing cold-water supply pipe is connected to the valve of the cistern and an overflow warning pipe is run outside the building or run to discharge over the pan or onto the floor where the W.C. is fitted internally.

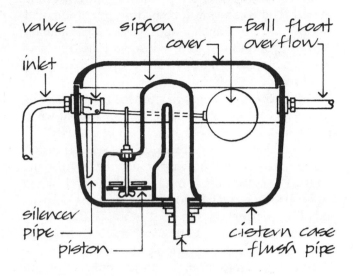

9 litre W.C. flushing cistern

Fig. 57

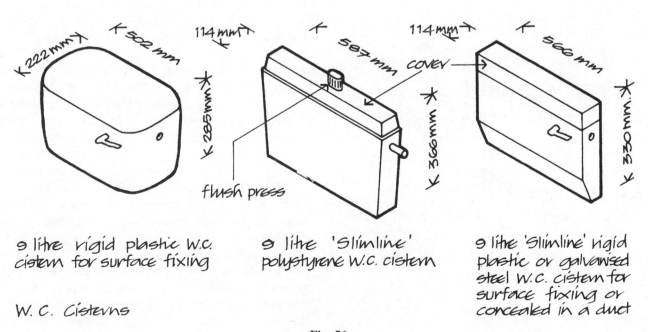

9 litre rigid plastic W.C. cistern for surface fixing

9 litre 'Slimline' polystyrene W.C. cistern

9 litre 'Slimline' rigid plastic or galvanised steel W.C. cistern for surface fixing or concealed in a duct

W.C. Cisterns

Fig. 56

W.C. flushing cisterns may use up to 40% of total domestic water consumption and it is wasteful to use 9 litres of water to flush urine out of a pan. The dual-flush cistern is designed to discharge either $4\frac{1}{2}$ or 9 litres.

The Water Supply Byelaws, that come into effect in 1988, will gradually phase out cisterns designed to give a 9 litres flush and those designed to give a dual flush, in favour of cisterns giving a 7.5 litres flush in one go. The Byelaws will come into operation on 1 January 1991 in England and Wales and 1 January 1993 in Scotland for all new installations. Replacements of cisterns alone of up to 9.5 litres capacity will be permitted.

A dual-flush cistern is illustrated in Fig. 58. The siphon has an air tube connected to it so that when the flush lever is pulled quickly and released the siphon action operates to discharge $4\frac{1}{2}$ litres and then stops by the entry of air through the air tube, the mouth of which is just above the $4\frac{1}{2}$ litre level. When the flush lever is pulled and held, the piston closes the end of the air tube and the whole 9 litres is discharged in one go. Where users are given instructions in the use of this cistern there is appreciable saving of water. The dual flush cistern will be gradually phased out, in common with the 9 litre cistern.

Flushing cisterns are made of enamelled or galvanised pressed steel or of plastics or of vitreous china.

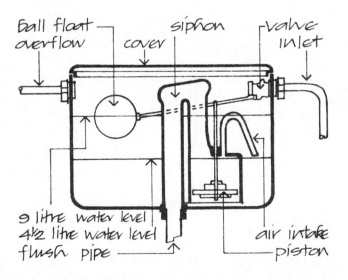

Dual flush W.C. cistern

Fig. 58

High-level and low-level cisterns are usually of pressed steel or plastic and close-coupled of vitreous china to match the material of the W.C. pan. Galvanised steel cisterns are used for fixing inside ducts behind the W.C. pan.

Small bore-macerator-sanitary system: The Building Regulations 1985, Part G. Hygiene, permit the use of small bore pipe discharges from W.C.s. The use of small bore pipe discharges to W.C.s has been in use in Europe for many years.

The use of a small bore pipe discharge for W.C.s depends on the use of a macerator and pump fitted to the outlet of W.C. pans. The electrically powered macerator and pump come into operation as the normal flush of a W.C. pan, by a conventional cistern, fills the pan. A macerator is a rotary shredder whose blades rotate at 3,000 rpm and reduce solid matter to pulp, which is, with the flush water, then pumped along a small (18 to 22 mm) pipe to the discharge stack.

The macerator (shredder) and pump unit, which is about 340 × 270 × 165 mm, fits conveniently behind a W.C. pan. The unit is connected to the horizontal outlet of a BS 5503 pan and a small bore outlet pipe. The macerator and pump are connected to a fixed, fused electrical outlet.

The particular advantage of the small bore system is in fitting a W.C., in either an existing or a new building some distance from the nearest foul water drainage stack, with a small bore (18 to 22 mm) pipe that can be run in floors or be easily boxed in. In addition, because of the pumped discharge, the small bore branch discharge pipe can carry the discharge for up to 20 metres with a minimum fall of 1 in 180 and can also pump the discharge vertically up to 4 metres, with a reduced horizontal limit, which is of considerable advantage in fitting W.C.s in basements below drain levels.

The macerator and pump unit can also be used to boost the discharge from other fittings such as baths, basins, sinks, bidets and urinals along small bore runs, with a minimum fall, and over considerable runs not suited to normal gravity discharge.

The small bore discharge system is not a substitute for the normal short run branch discharge pipe system for fittings grouped closely around a vertical foul water drainage system, because of the additional cost of the macerator and pump unit and the need for frequent periodic maintenance of the unit.

Fig. 59 is an illustration of a macerator and pump unit applied to a W.C. pan.

Urinals: The three types of urinal in general use are the slab urinal, stall urinal and bowl urinal, as illustrated in Fig. 60. The slab urinal consists of a flat slab fixed against a wall, projecting return end slabs and a trough. The slab may be flush or with divisions as illustrated in Fig. 60. This is the cheapest, most straightforward and hygienic of urinals.

The stall urinal comprises individual curved stalls each with an integral channel, the junction between the individual stalls being covered by rolls as illustrated in Fig. 60. The stall urinal is heavy, takes up more space than the slab and is more difficult to

clean. It is made of a robust material less liable to damage than the slab.

The bowl urinal consists of individual bowls mounted on the wall as illustrated in Fig. 60. The bowls are fixed individually with or without division pieces. Bowl urinals are used for their neat appearance where they are not liable to damage or misuse.

Slab and bowl urinals are made of vitreous china and stalls of glazed fireclay.

Urinals are flushed by automatic flushing cisterns fixed above the urinal and discharging through a flush pipe, spreaders or sparge pipe as illustrated in Fig. 60. The automatic flushing cistern is of 4.5 litres capacity per slab, stall or bowl and the cisterns are adjusted to flush every 20 minutes.

The Water Supply Byelaws, that come into effect in 1988, limit the flush of cisterns, to two or more urinal units, to 7.5 litres per hour for each unit and 10 litres per hour for one urinal unit.

The cistern is filled directly from the distributing pipe, the rate of filling and therefore the frequency of flush being controlled by a valve. When full the siphon overturns and discharges the contents in one go. The flush from the cistern, down the flush pipe is then distributed over the urinal by the individual

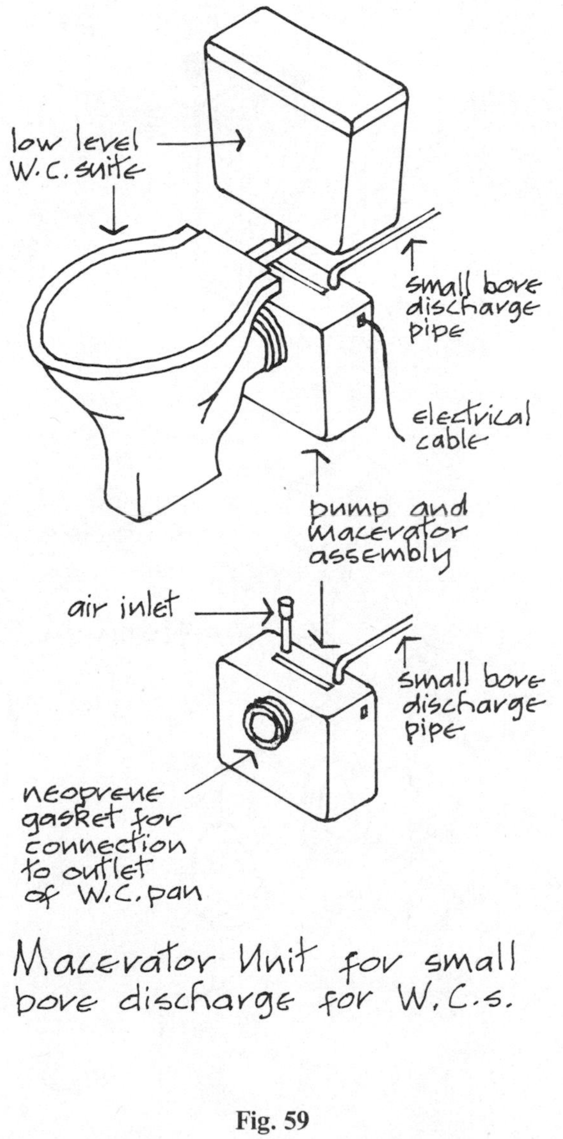

low level
W.C. suite

small bore
discharge
pipe

electrical
cable

pump and
macerator
assembly

air inlet

small bore
discharge
pipe

neoprene
gasket for
connection
to outlet
of W.C. pan

Macerator Unit for small
bore discharge for W.C.s

Fig. 59

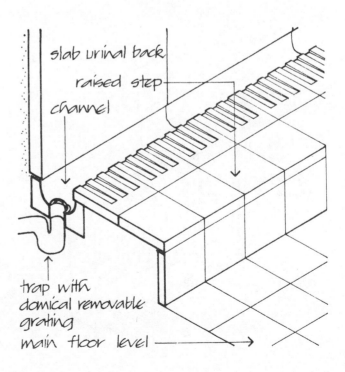

slab urinal back
raised step
channel

trap with
domical removable
grating
main floor level →

Fig. 61

49

spreaders to each slab, stall or bowl or by means of a perforated pipe, termed a sparge pipe to slab urinals only.

One outlet to trap and branch discharge pipe is used for up to six stalls or slab units, the outlet being in the channel to the slab or in the channel of one of the stall units. The outlet, 40 mm, minimum diameter is covered with a domed gun metal grating and the outlet connected to a trap and waste. Deposits build up rapidly in the trap of urinals and traps of glazed ceramic, vitreous enamel or lead are often used to take the corrosive cleaning agents used.

To accommodate the channel of urinals in a floor a step is often formed. Fig. 61 is an illustration of a typical urinal slab showing channel, trap and waste.

Bowl urinal outlets are often connected to a combined waste with a running trap.

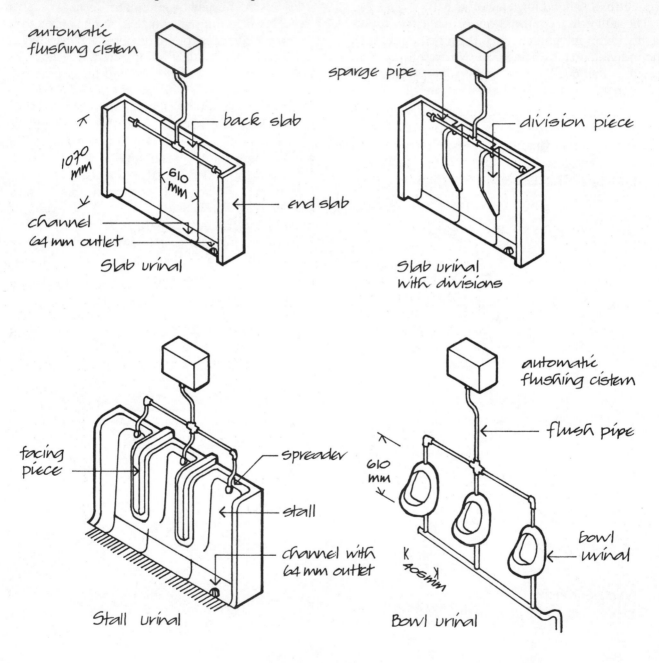

Fig. 60

WASTE APPLIANCES

Wash basins designed for washing the upper part of the body, are supported by wall brackets or on a pedestal secured to the floor as illustrated in Fig. 62.

The standard wash basin consists of a bowl, soap tray, outlet, water overflow connected to the outlet and holes for fixing taps as illustrated in Fig. 63. The usual wall-mounted basin is fixed on enamelled cast-iron brackets screwed to wood plugs in the wall. The more expensive pedestal basin consists of a basin and a separate vitreous china pedestal that is screwed to the floor and on which the basin is mounted. The purpose of the pedestal is to hide the trap, waste and hot and cold service pipes.

The majority of wash basins are made of vitreous china. A wide range of sizes and designs of wash basins is available ranging from small corner basins and hand basins to basins large enough to bath a small child. In recent years plastic basins have been made which are suited in particular to fitting to stands and working tops.

Hot and cold pillar taps connected to 12 or 15 mm hot and cold distributing or supply pipes are fixed to or over wash basins. To prevent the possibility of fouled water in the basin being back siphoned into the pipes it will be a requirement of the Water Supply Byelaws that there be an air gap between the outlet of the taps and the spill over or top edge of the basin as described in chapter 1.

A P trap with a 75-mm water seal is fitted to wash basins with a 32-mm waste.

Towards the end of the discharge, wash-basin wastes may run full bore, and the consequent self-siphonage empty the water seal from the trap. Because of the shape of the basin bowl there is not sufficient tail-off water to refill the trap. To avoid loss of water seal it is necessary to limit the length of wastes.

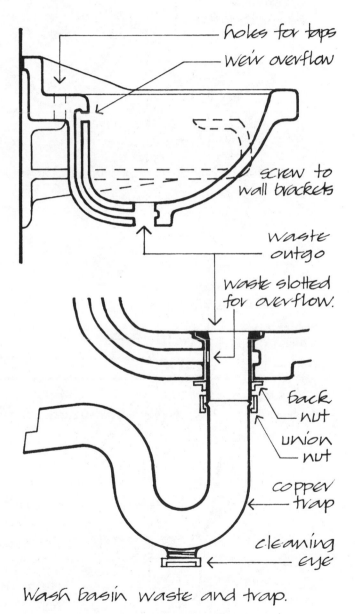

Wash basin waste and trap.

Fig. 63

Wash basin fixed on wall brackets.

Wash basin on pedestal.

Fig. 62

Baths: The type of bath most used is the standard Magnå square ended bath, illustrated in Fig. 64. These baths are made of porcelain-enamelled cast iron or pressed-sheet steel or of plastic. The enamel finish of the heavier and more rigid cast-iron bath is less likely to be damaged than that on the lighter pressed steel bath. The plastic bath does not have the hard bright finish of the metal bath, is fairly readily scratched and is lightweight and not liable to rust.

The Magna bath has a rectangular profile rim designed to accommodate end and side panels, and an outlet, overflow, holes for taps and adjustable feet as illustrated in Fig. 65.

Roll top or tub baths illustrated in Fig. 64 are little used today because of the comparatively large volume of water required to fill them and the difficulty of fitting side and end panels.

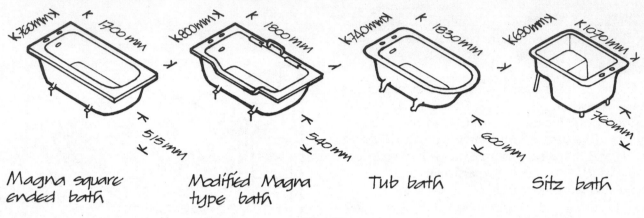

Magna square ended bath

Modified Magna type bath

Tub bath

Sitz bath

Fig. 64

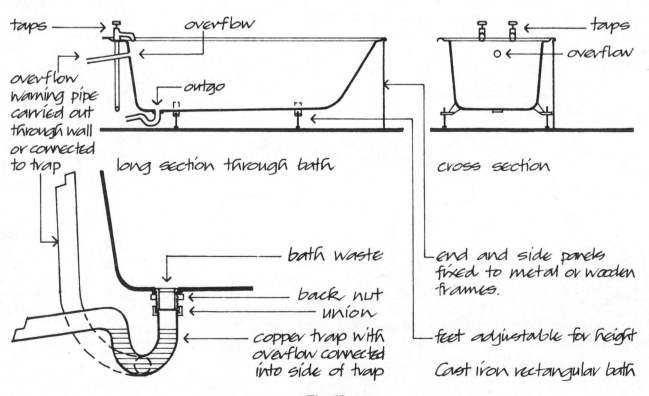

taps

overflow

overflow warning pipe carried out through wall or connected to trap

outgo

long section through bath

taps

overflow

cross section

bath waste

back nut

union

copper trap with overflow connected into side of trap

end and side panels fixed to metal or wooden frames.

feet adjustable for height

Cast iron rectangular bath

Fig. 65

Sitz or sitting baths have a stepped bottom to form a seat as illustrated in Fig. 64 and may be used where space is restricted. This type of bath is little used.

Baths are fixed on adjustable feet against a wall or in a recess with side and end panels of preformed board, plastic or metal secured to wood or metal brackets or frames. The plaster or tile wall finish is brought down to the top of the bath rim. In time, particularly on timber floors, the joint between the top of the bath and the plaster or tile will crack.

The discharge from a bath is unlikely to run full bore and cause self-siphonage and loss of water seal to the trap and if the trap were to lose its seal by siphonage it would be filled by the tail-off water from the flat bottom of the bath. The length and slope of a bath waste is therefore not critical. A 75-mm seal trap is fitted to the bath waste and connected to the 40-mm waste.

An overflow pipe is connected to the bath and either run through an outside wall as overflow warning pipe or connected to the bath outlet or trap as illustrated in Fig. 65. Overflow warning pipes run through an outside wall should have hinged flaps else an appreciable cold draught may blow into the bath.

The 18-mm cold and hot distributing or supply pipes are connected to either individual pillar taps, a mixer with taps or a shower fitting or both with an air gap between the outlet and spillover level of bath, similar to that for basins.

Where shower fittings are provided the wall or walls over the baths should be finished in some impermeable material such as tile and a waterproof curtain be provided.

Showers: The conventional shower or shower bath consists of a shower tray or receiver of glazed ceramic, enamelled cast iron or plastic to collect and discharge water, with a fixed or hand-held shower head or rose and mixing valves. The shower is either fixed in a wall recess or may be free standing with enamelled metal or plastic sides. The walls around fixed showers are lined with some impermeable material such as tile and the open side fitted with a waterproof curtain. Fig. 66 is an illustration of shower trays. The tray with a waste and no overflow is for use as a shower only. The tray with a waste plug and an overflow is for use either as a shower or a foot bath.

The shower tray may be fixed onto or be recessed in the floor. A 75-mm seal trap is fitted to the tray

and connected to a 40-mm waste. The discharge from a shower tray is unlikely to run full bore down the waste and as there is little likelihood of self-siphonage the length and slope of the waste is not critical.

The Water Supply Byelaws that come into effect in 1988 require a double check valve assembly to both hot and cold supply pipes to showers, where the head can be lowered below the spillover level of appliances.

Sinks for domestic purposes are made of enamelled cast iron or pressed steel, stainless steel, cast acrylic sheet or glazed fireclay. Stainless steel is the most durable material. An enamelled finish to rigid cast iron is less likely to suffer damage than to less rigid

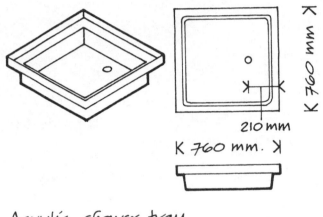

Acrylic shower tray

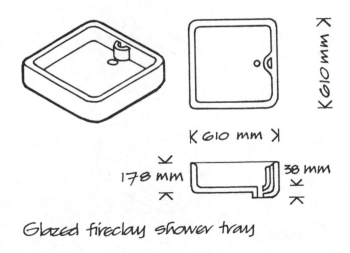

Glazed fireclay shower tray

Fig. 66

pressed steel. Acrylic is liable to damage by hot utensils. Glazed fireclay is very heavy and liable to chipping particularly at the edges and is little used today.

Sinks may consist of a bowl, a bowl with integral drainer, double bowl and integral drainers or bowl with double drainer as illustrated in Fig. 67.

Sinks may have outlets and weir overflows joined to the outlet. The 15-mm drinking supply from the service main and the 15-mm hot-water distributing pipe are joined to pillar taps or mixing valve and taps

fixed to holes in the sink top or mounted over the sink. A 75 mm seal trap is fixed to the sink outlet and connected to the 40-mm waste. The sink waste is unlikely to run full bore and cause self-siphonage. If the water seal of the trap was to be overturned by siphonage, then the tail-off water from the flat bottom of the sink would fill the trap. The length and slope of a sink waste is, therefore, not critical.

Most sinks are designed to be fitted to sink units framed from wood or metal into which the sink fits, and on which it is supported.

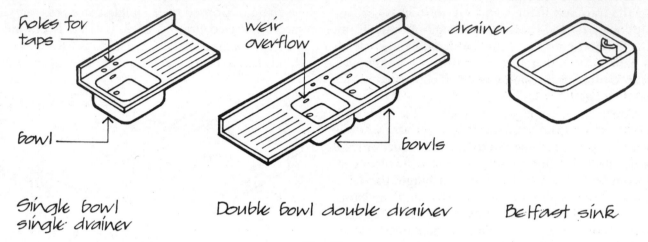

Single bowl single drainer

Double bowl double drainer

Belfast sink

Fig. 67

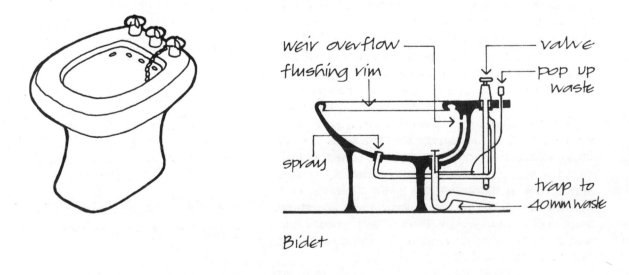

Bidet

Fig. 68

Bidet

Fig. 69

Bidets are appliances for washing the excretory organs. They consist of a bowl or pan shaped for the purpose with an integral pedestal base as illustrated in Fig. 68 and are made of vitreous china or stainless steel. Bidets are fitted with an outlet, hot and cold supply and either an ascending spray as illustrated in Fig. 69 or a hand-held shower.

To prevent contamination of mains water the Water Supply Byelaws that come into effect in 1988 require air gaps to taps to bidets and either a cistern feed or other effective device to feeds to sprays and showers. The 12 or 15 mm cold and hot-distributing supplies are connected to the taps and spray. A 75-mm seal trap is fitted to the outlet and connected to the 32-mm waste. The discharge from a bidet is unlikely to run full bore in the waste, and there is little likelihood of self-siphonage. The length and the slope of the waste to bidets is therefore not critical.

Traps are designed to contain a water seal against odours rising from sanitary pipework and drains. The simplest form of trap is a double bend in pipework, as illustrated in Fig. 70, the seal being the height between the top of the first bend and the bottom of the second. Traps are either 'P' or 'S' section, the former having a near horizontal outgo and the latter a vertical outgo.

W.C. pans have an integral trap to contain a water seal. All other sanitary appliances are fitted with a trap that is connected to the outlet of the appliance and to which the branch discharge pipe is connected. With the single-stack system of sanitary pipework a trap with a 75-mm seal is fitted to all sanitary appliances other than W.C. pans which have a 50-mm seal. Traps that are in one piece have a cleaning eye as illustrated in Fig. 70. The advantage of the two-piece trap (Fig. 70) is that it can be adjusted to suit various positions of the branch discharge pipe, and it can also be disconnected to clear blockages.

The resealing traps illustrated in Fig. 71 are designed to allow air through the trap in the case of the McAlpine trap and through the upper air tube as in the case of the Grevak trap when siphonage occurs, so that the reservoir of water is retained and reseals the trap when siphonage stops. These traps are more liable to blockages than ordinary traps, and are now little used when single-stack systems of pipework are installed.

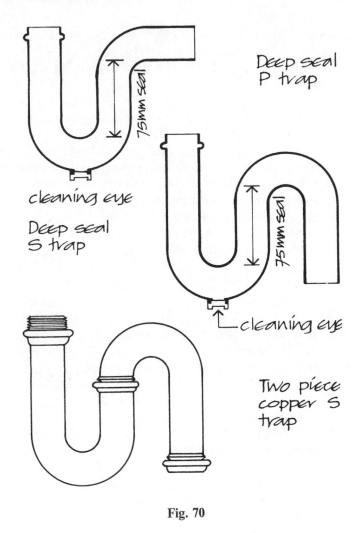

Deep seal P trap

cleaning eye

Deep seal S trap

75mm seal

cleaning eye

Two piece copper S trap

Fig. 70

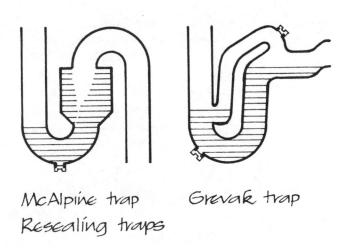

McAlpine trap

Grevak trap

Resealing traps

Fig. 71

CHAPTER THREE

SANITARY PIPEWORK

History: Up to the middle of the nineteenth century few buildings had a supply of water piped above ground-floor level. Water closets were either inside or outside at ground level and washing water was carried by jug to basins. From about the middle of the nineteenth century, due to improved pumping techniques, piped water increasingly extended above ground-floor level, first to water closets and later to wash basins and baths. This improvement in sanitary and washing facilities was helped by the mass production of sanitary appliances.

The drainage above ground of water closets was usually separate from that of other sanitary appliances. The demands for hygienic arrangements, provoked by the typhus epidemics early in the century, were at first confined to the drainage of water closets. Waste water from basins and baths was not at that time thought to be foul and the drains from waste-water appliances were often connected to rainwater pipes and drained to soakaways. To avoid drain smell, pipes from sanitary appliances were run directly out of buildings to vertical pipe systems fixed to external walls. A typical arrangement of the

drainpipes of this period is illustrated in Fig. 72. It will be seen that the first-floor W.C. discharges to a separate soil pipe connected to the drains. The waste water from the first-floor bath and basin, discharges into an open hopper head that also collects the rainwater from the roof with the hopper head draining to a trapped gulley connected to the drains. The advantage of this system is simplicity. The trapped gulley taking the discharge of rainwater and waste water acts as an effective seal against odours rising from the drains. As the bath and basin wastes discharge over the hopper head they do not need a trap. By combining rain and waste water the dis-

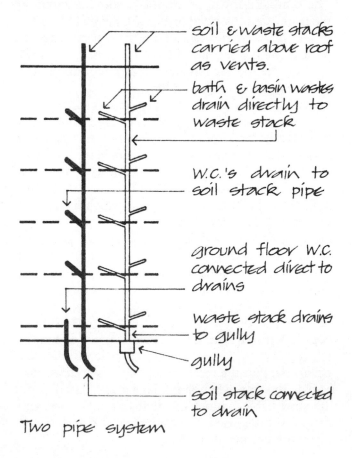

Two pipe system

Fig. 73

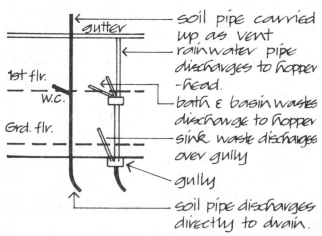

Two pipe system

Fig. 72

charge pipe is reasonably flushed. The one disadvantage of the system is that with careless use the hopper head may become fouled, smelly and eventually blocked. It is a simple matter to clear a hopper head at first floor level. The system of using hopper heads to collect waste-water discharges was also used for buildings over two floors in height and it was then that the smells from fouled hopper heads, floods from blocked heads, and the difficulty of clearing hopper heads above ground gave this system a bad name. The use of hopper heads for the collection of waste water has since been abandoned. The use of a separate discharge pipe for W.C.s and another for waste-water discharges was described as the two-pipe system. When the use of open hopper heads lost favour, a two-pipe system of separate sealed waste and soil stack systems were adopted, as illustrated in Fig. 73. It will be seen that there are two separate discharge stacks, one for the W.C.s and another for waste-water discharges. Both pipe systems are sealed and each discharges separately to the drains, the soil stack directly and the waste stack through a trapped gulley. In this modification of the original two-pipe system, rainwater discharges were separated from the waste water as there were no longer hopper heads to collect the two discharges.

The discharge of water from sanitary appliances causes changes of air pressure in a sealed discharge pipe system. The inevitable pressure changes or fluctuations are not in general large or of long duration and it is now known that pressure fluctuations sufficient to unseal water traps can be avoided by careful design of the discharge system. The single-stack system in common use today is designed to that end.

When piped water and sanitary appliances were installed above ground from the middle of the nineteenth century it was known that there was a likelihood of siphonage of water from traps due to pressure fluctuations. From fear of drain smells precautions were taken to prevent the siphonage of water from traps by the use of puff pipes and later anti-siphon pipes (vent pipes). In the event the system of anti-siphon pipes became an intricate web of pipes festooned over buildings of the early twentieth century.

To prevent the siphonage or loss of the water seal in a trap it is only necessary to maintain equal air pressure on both sides of the trap to a sanitary appliance. The most straightforward way of doing

this is to connect a short length of pipe from the outgo side of the trap to the open air. The short length of pipe was called a puff pipe, presumably because it drew in and expelled a puff of air to stabilise pressure. The use of a puff pipe to the trap of a W.C. and a basin is illustrated in Fig. 74. The use of puff pipes to W.C. pan traps was quickly abandoned for fear of drain smells rising up the soil pipe through the puff pipe and into an open window above. It would obviously need a singularly pungent smell propelled by considerable air pressure to perform this near miracle. None the less, the fear of drain smells that has to this day beggared rationalisation of drains, caused the puff pipe to be abandoned. Recently puff pipes have been used to ventilate a discharge pipe system in a building with sealed windows and the most recent regulations permit the use of anit-siphon valves, that are a form of puff pipe.

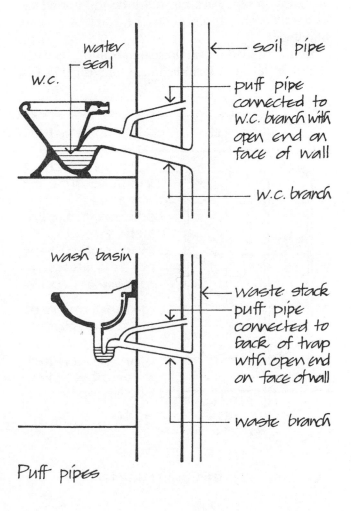

Fig. 74

Having condemned the puff pipe, the then accepted means of preventing siphonage of the water seal of traps was the anti-siphon pipe (now called the vent pipe). A separate system of pipes was connected to the trap of all sanitary appliances to equalise air pressure on both sides of the traps. Fig. 75 illustrates anti-siphon pipe systems applied to a two-pipe system of pipework. It will be seen that there is a separate anti-siphon or vent pipe system to each stack with branches from the vent pipes connected to the outlet side of each trap to each appliance. This fully vented two-pipe system was commonly installed in buildings between the world wars.

This unsightly and uneconomic web of pipes was modified in the one-pipe system which utilised a single discharge stack for the discharge from all appliances. Fig. 76 illustrates a fully vented one-pipe system. The one-pipe system provided some small economy in pipe runs but did little to improve the unsightly web of pipes on the external face of buildings.

In 1952 the Building Research Station, now the Building Research Establishment, published its first report on sanitary pipework. For some years the station had been carrying out tests in the laboratory and on site to determine the likelihood of siphonage of traps to appliances with a view to effecting economy in sanitary pipework in housing. The report established that by careful arrangement of the branches to a soil pipe there would be no loss of seal to the traps of appliances and therefore no need for vent pipes. The recommended single-soil pipe with branches from sanitary appliances without vent pipes was called the single-stack system, illustrated in Fig. 77. Since then further work has shown that the single-stack system can be used for multi-storey buildings without vent pipes by increasing the size of the stack or by the use of minimal vent pipes with a smaller stack.

From their study of sanitary pipe systems in use, the Research Station distinguished three conditions in which there could be loss of water seal to traps of appliances. These three conditions of air pressure fluctuation are induced siphonage, back pressure and self-siphonage.

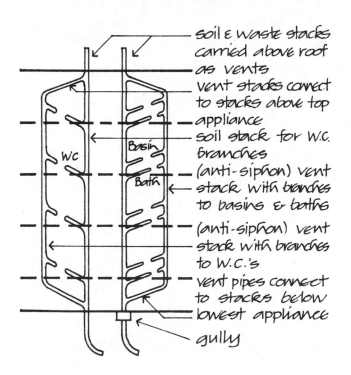

Two pipe system fully vented

Fig. 75

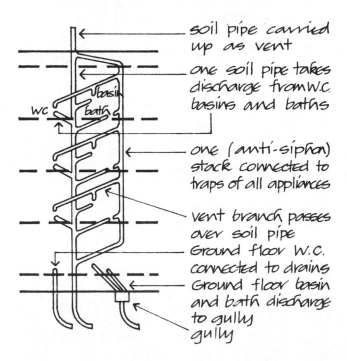

One pipe system fully vented

Fig. 76

Induced siphonage may be caused by a discharge from a W.C. down a soil stack. As the discharge carries air with it there is a momentary reduction in pressure that may unseal the trap to a branch waste as illustrated in Fig. 78. W.C. branches to stacks should be swept in the direction of flow as illustrated in Fig. 85 to reduce the likelihood of induced siphonage. Induced siphonage may also occur where waste pipes from two appliances connect to a common branch waste pipe.

Self-siphonage may occur where the discharge from an appliance runs full bore in the waste pipe at the end of the discharge, causes a reduction in pressure and possible loss of water seal to the trap as illustrated in Fig. 79. Where loss of water seal to wash-basin traps occurs, due to self-siphonage, the trap will not be filled because there is too little tail-off water from the funnel-shaped basin to fill the trap.

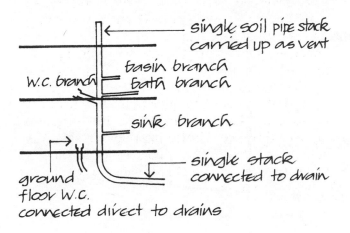

Single stack system.

Fig. 77

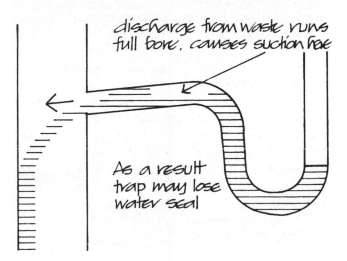

Self - siphonage

Fig. 79

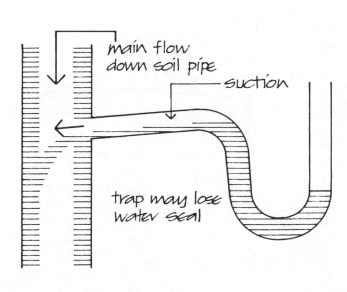

Induced siphonage

Fig. 78

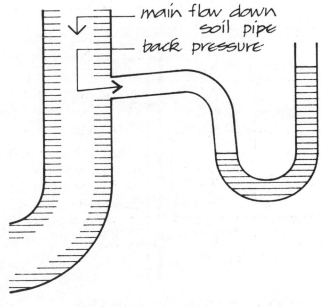

Back pressure

Fig. 80

To reduce the possibility of self-siphonage, wash-basin wastes should not be more than 1.7 m long. If the water seal to the traps of baths and sinks is broken by self-siphonage there is sufficient tail-off water from the flat bottom of these appliances to fill the trap and there is, therefore, no need to limit the length or slope of wastes against self-siphonage.

Back pressure occurs when a discharge reaches the base of a stack at the junction of a branch waste near the base of the stack. The increased pressure caused by the discharge may overturn the water seal in the trap to the branch waste as illustrated in Fig. 80. To limit back pressure the bend at the base of the stack should have a large radius as illustrated in Fig. 85. Similarly where a branch waste is connected close to a W.C. branch a discharge from the W.C. may cause back pressure in the branch waste. Branch wastes should not be connected to the stack for a depth of 200 mm below the centre line of the W.C. branch as illustrated in Fig. 88.

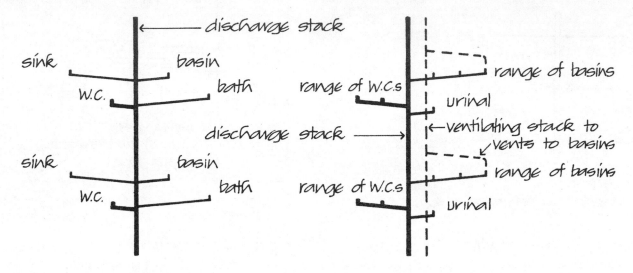

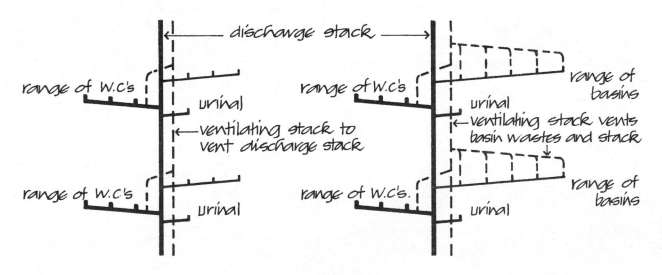

Fig. 81

Single-stack system: For economy of sanitary pipework the single-stack system is used today in both domestic and public buildings. Where pressure fluctuations in the stack may be so great as to cause induced siphonage or back pressure, for example, in multi-storey buildings, then a ventilation pipe connected to the stack is used. This arrangement is the ventilated stack system. Where pressure fluctuations in branch wastes to a single-stack system may be sufficient to siphon the water seal from traps then a ventilation pipe system is connected to vent the traps. This is the modified single-stack system. Where pressure fluctuations in the stack and the branch wastes cannot be limited to prevent self-siphonage, induced siphonage and back pressure, for example in multi-storey buildings, a ventilated system is used, the ventilating pipe system being connected to both the stack and the traps of appliances. Fig. 81 is an illustration of these four arrangements, the single-stack, modified single-stack, ventilated-stack and ventilated systems.

The single vertical pipe collecting discharges from all sanitary appliances is the discharge stack and the pipes from all appliances to the stack, discharge pipes. The single vertical ventilating pipe is the ventilating or vent stack and the branches from it to the discharge stack and discharge pipes, ventilating or vent pipes.

Fig. 82 illustrates the application of the single stack to a five-floor residential building with one group of appliances on each floor. The discharge pipes are arranged within the limitations set out in Fig. 80.

In residential multi-storey buildings of up to twenty floors a single 100-mm stack may be used for two groups of appliances per floor with a single ventilation stack connected to the stack or to a W.C.

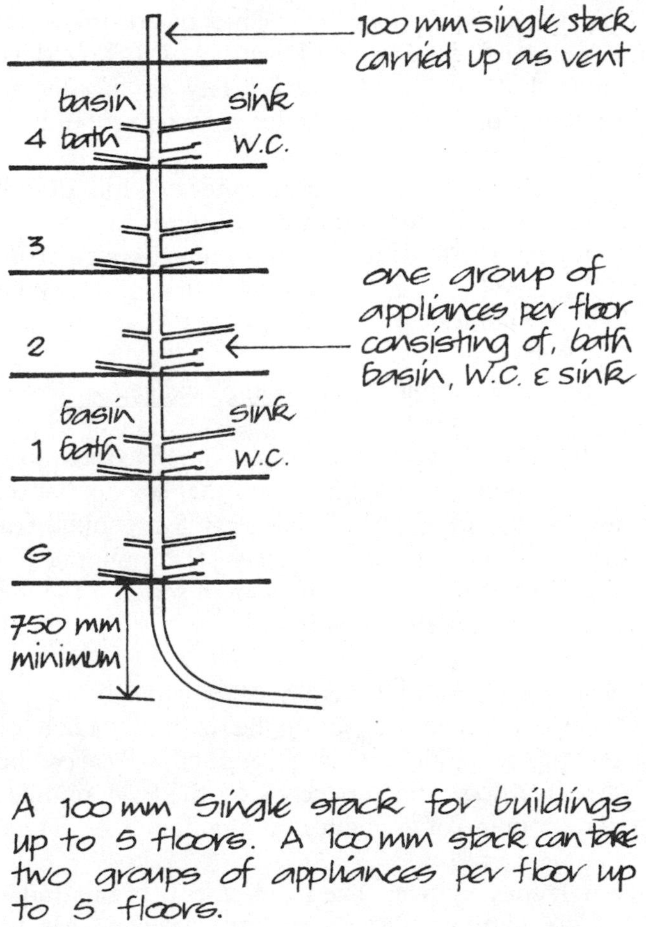

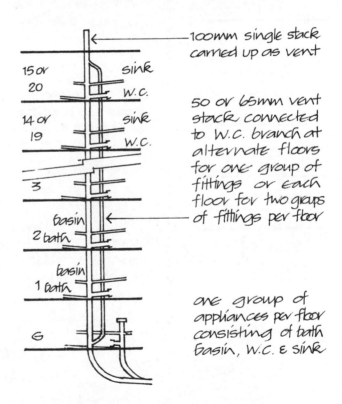

A 100 mm single stack for buildings up to 5 floors. A 100 mm stack can take two groups of appliances per floor up to 5 floors.

Single stack for up to 20 floors

Fig. 82

Fig. 83

discharge pipe on alternate floors for one group of appliances per floor or to each floor for two groups of appliances per floor as illustrated in Fig. 83. The vent stack is used to limit pressure fluctuations in the discharge stack to reduce induced siphonage and back pressure. This is an example of the ventilated stack system. As an alternative, a larger discharge stack, 150 mm may be used without a vent stack. The increase in the size of the discharge stack limits pressure fluctuations in the stack to the extent that ventilation is not necessary. For residential buildings up to twenty floors there should be a large radius bend at the foot of the stack of larger diameter than the stack or ground-floor appliances should be connected directly to the drains or to a separate stack. For buildings over twenty floors all appliances on the ground and first floors should be connected to a separate stack as illustrated in Fig. 84.

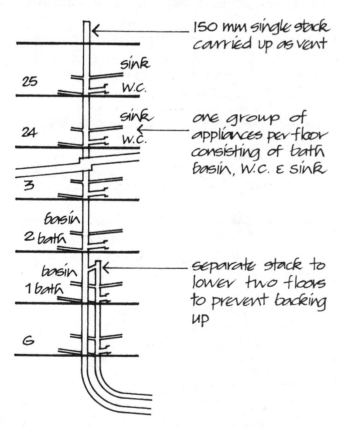

Single stack for up to 25 floors.

Fig. 84

SANITARY PIPEWORK

Section 1 of the approved document H1 gives practical guidance to meeting the requirements of the Building Regulations 1985 for sanitary pipework.

The approved documents give practical guidance to meeting the requirements of the Building Regulations, but there is no obligation to adopt any particular solution given in the documents if the requirements of the Regulations can be satisfactorily met in some other way.

Sanitary pipework includes all pipework used to carry the discharge of 'foul water' from sanitary appliances such as water closets, bidets, baths, wash basins and sinks and ventilation pipework as is necessary to prevent foul air from the drainage system entering the building under working conditions.

An acceptable level of performance of sanitary pipework and drainage will be met by any provision of section 1 of Approved Document H1. To reduce the risk to the health and safety of persons in buildings the foul water drainage system should:

(a) convey the flow of foul water to a foul outfall
(b) minimise the risk of blockage or leakage
(c) prevent foul air from the drainage system from entering the building under working conditions
(d) be ventilated
(e) be accessible for clearing blockages

In the document, 'foul water' is defined as waste from a sanitary convenience or other soil appliance, and water which has been used for cooking or washing, but does not include waste containing any trade effluent. Foul outfall means a sewer, cesspool, septic tank or settlement tank.

Sanitary pipework generally: The capacity of the pipework, which depends on the size and gradient of the pipes, should be large enough to carry the expected flow, which depends on the type, number and grouping of appliances at any point.

Single stack system: The requirements of the Building Regulations 1985 for sanitary pipework can be met by the use of the single stack system of sanitary pipework, which is the system most in use for economy in layout and use of pipework. Fig. 85, is an

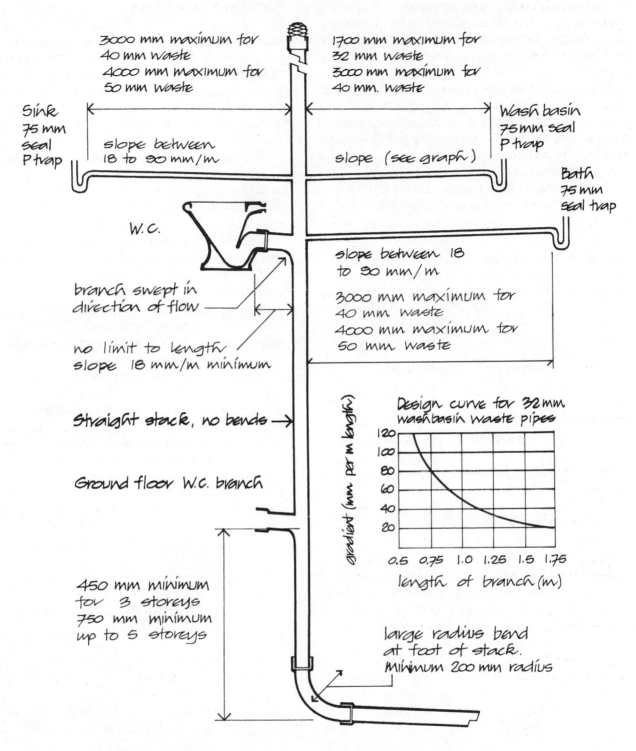

3000 mm maximum for
40 mm waste
4000 mm maximum for
50 mm waste

1700 mm maximum for
32 mm waste
3000 mm maximum for
40 mm. waste

Sink
75 mm
seal
P trap

slope between
18 to 90 mm/m

slope (see graph)

Wash basin
75 mm seal
P trap

Bath
75 mm
seal trap

W.C.

branch swept in
direction of flow

no limit to length
slope 18 mm/m minimum

slope between 18
to 90 mm/m

3000 mm maximum for
40 mm waste
4000 mm maximum for
50 mm waste

Straight stack, no bends →

Ground floor W.C. branch

Design curve for 32 mm
washbasin waste pipes

gradient (mm per m length)

120
100
80
60
40
20

0.5 0.75 1.0 1.25 1.5 1.75

length of branch (m)

450 mm minimum
for 3 storeys
750 mm minimum
up to 5 storeys

large radius bend
at foot of stack.
minimum 200 mm radius

Single stack system

Fig. 85

illustration of a single stack system for a two storey house, showing a single discharge stack pipe to which are connected branch discharge pipes from a sink, wash basin, W.C., bath and ground floor W.C.

Traps: Where sanitary appliances discharge foul water to the sanitary pipework system there should be a water seal, provided by means of a trap, to prevent foul air from entering the building under working conditions.

It will be seen that there is a water seal trap to each of the appliances. The minimum size and depth of water seal to these traps is set out in Table 5.

Table 5. Minimum trap sizes and seal depths

Appliance	Diameter of trap [mm]	Depth of seal [mm]
washbasin bidet	32	75
sink bath shower food waste disposal unit urinal bowl	40	75
wc pan	(min dimension) 75	50

Water closet pans have a water seal trap that is integral with the pan in the form of a single or double water seal as illustrated in Figs 48 and 49. Baths, bidets, sinks and wash basins have a trap which is fitted to the appliance and connected to the branch discharge pipe. Single and double seal traps are illustrated in Figs 70 and 71. To facilitate clearing blockages there should be a clearing eye or the trap should be removable as illustrated in Fig. 70.

To prevent the water seal in traps being broken by the pressures that can develop in a sanitary pipe system, the length and gradient of branch discharge pipes should be limited to those set out in Fig. 85, or a system of ventilating pipes should be used.

Branch discharge pipes: The discharge of foul water from sanitary appliances is carried to the vertical

discharge stack by branch pipes as illustrated in Fig. 85. All branch discharge pipes should discharge into a discharge stack except those to appliances on the ground floor. Ground floor sinks, baths and wash basins may discharge to a gully and W.C.s, bidets and urinals to a drain. A branch pipe from a ground floor W.C. should only discharge directly to a drain if the drop is less than 1.5 metres as illustrated in Fig. 86.

A branch pipe should not discharge into a stack lower than 450 above the invert of the tail of the bend at the foot of the stack for single dwellings up to three storeys and 750 for buildings up to five storeys' height.

The branch pipes from more than one ground floor appliance may discharge to an unvented stub stack with the stub stack connected to a ventilated discharge stack or a drain, provided no branch is more than 2 metres above the invert of the connection to the drain and branches from a closet more than 1.5 metres from the crown of the closet trap as illustrated in Fig. 87.

Branch pipes from waste water fittings such as sinks, baths and basins on the ground floor should discharge to a gully between the grating and the top level of the water seal.

To avoid cross flow, small similar sized connections not directly opposite should be offset by 110 on a 100 stack and 250 on a 150 stack as illustrated in Fig 88. A waste water branch should not enter the stack within 200 below a W.C. connection as illustrated in Fig. 88.

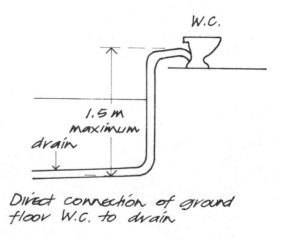

Direct connection of ground floor W.C. to drain

Fig. 86

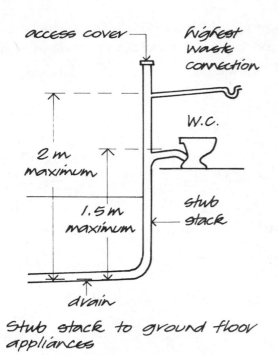

Stub stack to ground floor appliances

Fig. 87

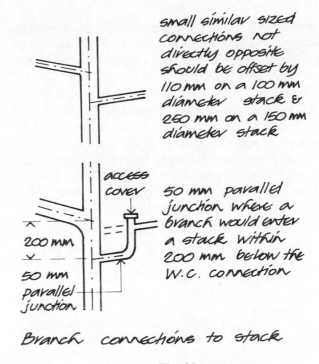

Branch connections to stack

Fig. 88

Size of branch pipes: Pipes serving single appliances should be at least the same diameter as the appliance trap and the diameter shown in Table 6 if it serves more than one appliance and is unventilated.

Bends in branch pipes, which should be avoided if possible, should have a radius as large as possible and have a centre line radius of at least 75 for pipes of 65 or less diameter.

Junctions on branch pipes should be made with a sweep of 25 radius or at an angle of 45° and connections of branch pipes of 75 diameter or more, to the stack should be made with a sweep of 50 minimum radius or at 45°.

Ventilation of branch pipes: It is not necessary to provide ventilation to branch pipes whose length and slope is limited to the figures given in Fig. 85, or to the common branch discharge pipes set out in Table 6. Where the length or slope is greater than these limits, the branch pipes should be ventilated by a

Table 6. Common branch discharge pipes (unvented)

Appliance	Max number to be connected	OR	Max length of branch [m]	Min size of pipe [mm]	Gradient limits (fall per metre) min [mm]		max [mm]
W.C.s	8		15	100	9	to	90
urinals: bowls	5		*	50	18	to	90
stalls	6		*	65	18	to	90
washbasins	4		4 (no bends)	50	18	to	45

Note
* No limitation as regards venting but should be as short as possible.

branch ventilation pipe to external air, to a discharge stack or to a ventilating stack where the number of ventilating pipes and their distance to a discharge stack are large.

Branch ventilating pipes should be connected to the discharge pipe within 300 of the trap and should not connect to the stack below the spillover level of the highest appliance served as illustrated in Fig. 89.

Branch ventilating pipes to branch pipes to branch pipes serving one appliance should be 25 diameter or where the branch is longer than 15 metres or has more than five bends, 32 diameter.

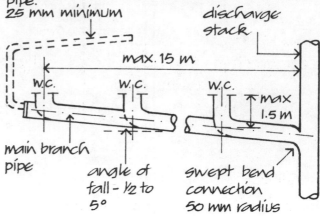

Range of W.C.'s branch discharge pipe

Fig. 90

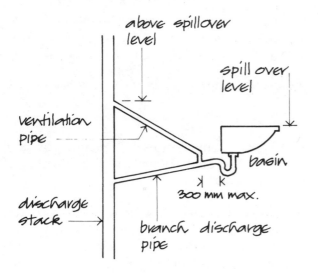

Branch ventilation pipe

Fig. 89

Ranges of W.C.s: Discharge pipes from ranges of W.C.s are usually 100 mm. The discharge pipes do not run full and there is little likelihood of self-siphonage of traps to appliances and, therefore, no need for venting. Ranges of eight or more W.C.s may be connected to a common discharge pipe. The shape and length of the common discharge pipe is not critical. The connection of the common discharge pipe to the stack should be through a swept bend and the connection of the W.C.s to the common discharge pipe should likewise be through a swept bend as illustrated in Fig. 90. Where there are more than 8 W.C.s in a range or more than two bends in the branch discharge pipe, a ventilating pipe may be necessary.

Ranges of wash basins: A range of up to four basins may be connected to a 50-mm common discharge pipe without venting as illustrated in Fig. 91 and up to five with one 25-mm vent to the highest point of the discharge pipe. With ranges of more than five basins it is necessary to vent the trap to each appliance to limit pressure fluctuations that might otherwise cause self-siphonage of the water seal to traps as illustrated in Fig. 92. The vent stack and pipes are connected to the discharge pipes to each appliance and the vent stack may be run to outside air independent of the discharge stack.

The discharge pipes from basins fitted with spray taps do not run full and there is, therefore, no likelihood of self-siphonage. Ranges of up to eight basins fitted with spray taps do not require ventilation of traps.

Urinals: The discharge pipe from urinals does not run full and there is no need for ventilation of traps. Discharge pipes to urinals should be as short as possible to minimise build up of deposits.

Ranges of W.C.s and basins and urinals on several floors may discharge to a common single stack without vent pipes when the estimated frequency of use of appliances and the consequent discharge loading of the pipe system is unlikely to cause gross pressure fluctuations. Where the discharge loading

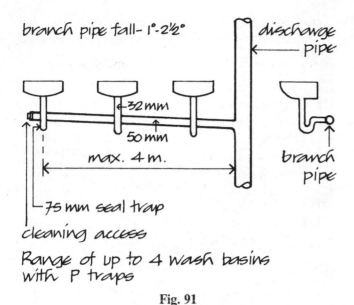

branch pipe fall- 1°-2½°

discharge pipe

←32mm

50mm

max. 4 m.

branch pipe

75 mm seal trap

cleaning access

Range of up to 4 wash basins with P traps

Fig. 91

require venting then the vent stack is connected both to the wash-basin traps and the discharge stack as in the ventilated system. Fig. 81 illustrates these arrangements. Which one is used will depend on the estimated frequency of use, assumed discharge loading and the size of the discharge stack. Alternatively, the vent stack may be connected to air independently of the discharge stack as in the modified single-stack system where the vent pipe system is used to limit pressure fluctuations in the discharge pipes to basins. Which system is used will depend on the estimated frequency of use, assumed discharge loading and the size of the discharge stack.

Discharge stacks: These should not have offsets in any part carrying foul water, should be run inside a building if it has more than 3 storeys and should discharge to a drain through a bend with as large a radius as possible and not less than 200 at the centre line, as illustrated in Fig. 85.

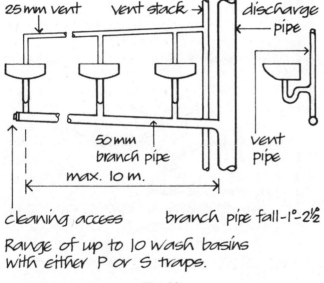

25 mm vent

vent stack →

discharge pipe

50 mm branch pipe

max. 10 m.

vent pipe

cleaning access   branch pipe fall-1°-2½

Range of up to 10 wash basins with either P or S traps.

Fig. 92

of the stack is likely to cause pressure fluctuations sufficient to cause induced siphonage or back pressure then a vent stack connected to the discharge stack at each floor is used to limit pressure fluctuations. Where the traps of ranges of wash basins have to be vented to avoid self-siphonage, the vent stack may be run to outside air independent of the discharge stack. Where both the discharge loading of the stack and the number of a range of wash basins

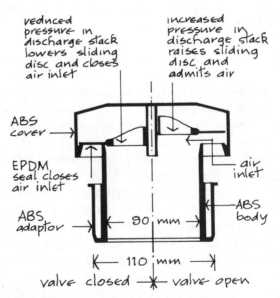

reduced pressure in discharge stack lowers sliding disc and closes air inlet

increased pressure in discharge stack raises sliding disc and admits air

ABS cover →

EPDM seal closes air inlet

air inlet

ABS adaptor

90 mm

ABS body

← 110 mm →

valve closed —✕— valve open

ABS [acrylonitrile butadiene styrene] air admittance valve for use with adaptor, reducer and ring seal coupling to upvc pipes.

Fig. 93

Discharge stacks should be ventilated to prevent water seals in traps being drawn by pressure that can develop in the system, by being continued up to outside air at least 900 above any opening in the building within 3 metres and finished with a cage or cover that does not restrict flow of air.

A discharge stack may terminate inside a building if it is fitted with an air admittance valve which is the subject of a current British Board of Agreement Certificate. An air admittance valve is illustrated in Fig. 93.

The dry part of a discharge stack above the highest branch, which serves only for ventilation, may be reduced to at least 75 diameter on one and two storey houses.

The size of the discharge stack is determined by the anticipated flow from all the fittings discharging into it.

Rodding points should be provided in the stack to give access to any length of pipe that cannot be reached from another part of the system.

PIPEWORK

The materials used for discharge pipework above ground are cast iron, copper, plastics and galvanised mild steel.

Unplasticised PVC is the most commonly used material for discharge stack and branch pipe systems for the low cost, ease of cutting and compact speedily made joints and the range of fittings available. This smooth surface material is usually finished in black or grey which requires no protective coating. The pipework is secured with loose brackets that are nailed or screwed to plugs in walls.

The usual method of jointing is by means of a solvent cement that is spread around pipe ends and welds the pipe to the fitting or by elastomeric ring seal joints. Fig. 94 is an illustration of uPVC discharge stack, branches and fittings suitable for a small house.

Cast-iron pipes are used for discharge pipework where the strength and durability of the material and the wide range of fittings available justifies the comparatively high initial cost. Where cast iron is used it is usual to run the discharge stack, W.C. discharge pipes and main branch pipes to ranges of fittings in cast iron and discharge pipes from waste

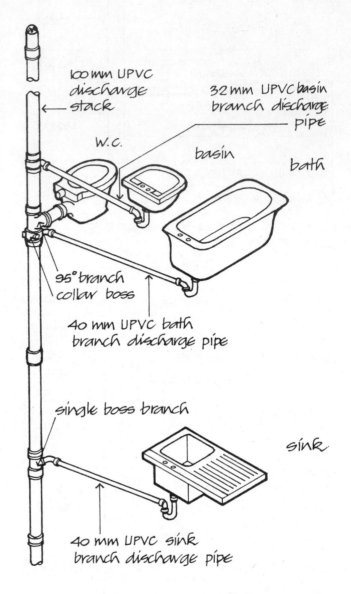

100 mm UPVC discharge stack

32 mm UPVC basin branch discharge pipe

W.C.

basin

bath

95° branch collar boss

40 mm UPVC bath branch discharge pipe

single boss branch

sink

40 mm UPVC sink branch discharge pipe

UPVC discharge stack and branches

Fig. 94

appliances in copper or plastic tube. In this way the strength and speed of fixing of cast iron is combined with the compact joints and ease of manipulation of copper or plastic pipe.

The pipes and fittings are sand cast or spun with socket and spigot ends as illustrated in Fig. 95 and are given a protective coating of tar or bitumen. A range of socket and spigot fittings with or without bolted access doors is provided. Joints are made with

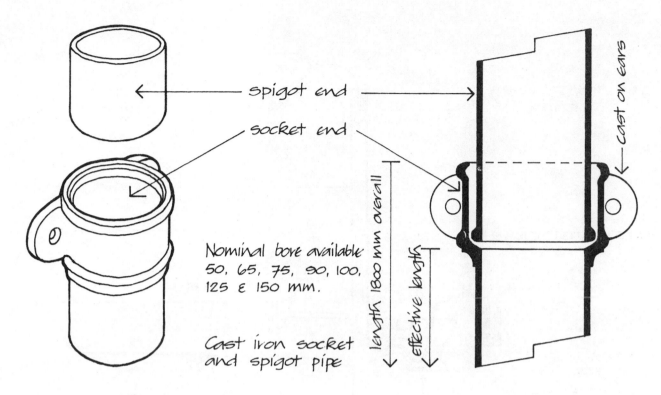

spigot end

socket end

Nominal bore available
50, 65, 75, 90, 100,
125 & 150 mm.

Cast iron socket
and spigot pipe

length 1800 mm overall

effective length

cast on ears

Fig. 95

molten lead which is caulked (rammed) into the joint that has been sealed with a gaskin of hemp, or with lead wool caulked fibre or a rubber seal ring. Pipes and fittings are usually fixed by nailing through cast on ears to plugs in walls and floors.

Copper pipe with capillary or compression joints is used for discharge pipes to waste appliances and vent stacks and pipes and copper pipes with brazed or welded joints are used for the larger discharge stack and W.C. discharge pipes. Prefabricated copper-pipe systems with brazed or welded joints are used for large installations where the high initial cost of the material is justified by its durability, compact joints, ease of manipulation and speed of erection. Fig. 96 illustrates a typical junction between a copper-discharge pipe and branch-discharge pipe.

Galvanised steel pipe is used mainly for discharge stacks where a prefabricated pipe with bossed entries for discharge pipes can be used to speed on site work. The use of these pipes depends on accurate setting out as there is no latitude in joints.

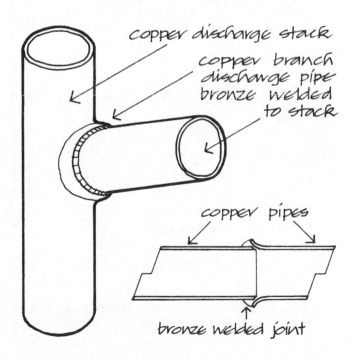

copper discharge stack

copper branch discharge pipe bronze welded to stack

copper pipes

bronze welded joint

Bronze welded joint

Fig. 96

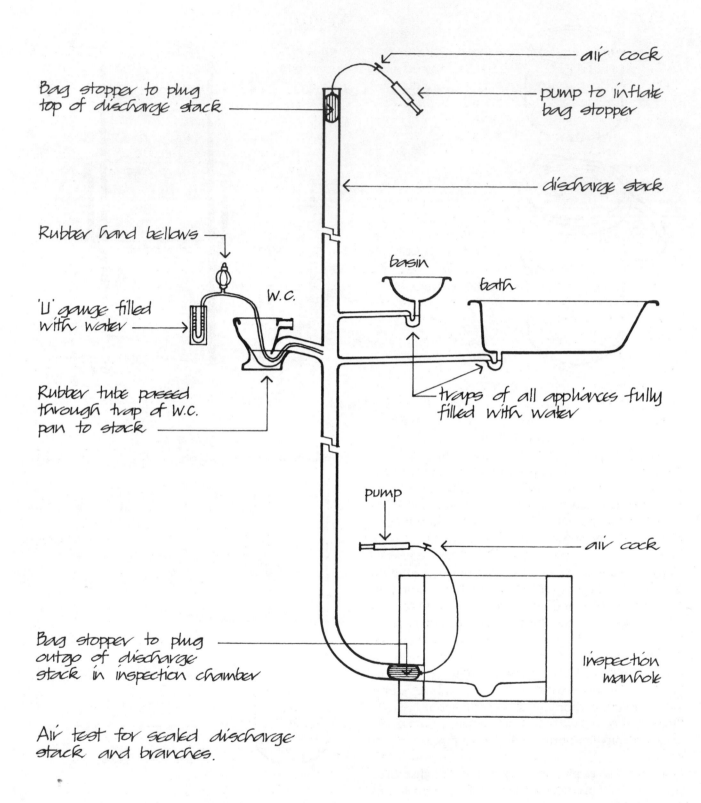

Bag stopper to plug top of discharge stack

air cock

pump to inflate bag stopper

discharge stack

Rubber hand bellows

basin

bath

'U' gauge filled with water

W.C.

Rubber tube passed through trap of W.C. pan to stack

traps of all appliances fully filled with water

pump

air cock

Bag stopper to plug outgo of discharge stack in inspection chamber

inspection manhole

Air test for sealed discharge stack and branches.

Fig. 97

TESTING

Soundness test (air test): The accepted method of testing the soundness of discharge stacks and pipes above ground is the air test. A sound pipe system will contain air under pressure for a few minutes as an indication of its capacity to contain the flow of liquid in conditions normal to a discharge-pipe system.

The air test is carried out to the whole discharge pipework above ground in one operation or where the pipework is extensive in two or more operations. The traps of all sanitary appliances are filled with water and the open ends of pipes are sealed with expanding drain plugs or bag stoppers. Air is pumped into the pipework through the W.C. pan trap and the air pressure measured on a 'U' tube water gauge or manometer. A pressure equal to 38-mm water gauge should be maintained for at least three minutes if the pipework is sound. Fig. 97 illustrates the equipment used for the air test.

If the air pressure is not maintained for three minutes, leaks may be traced by spreading a soap solution around joints, with the pipework under air pressure bubbles in the soap solution will indicate leaks or alternatively, smoke is pumped into the pipework from a smoke machine and escape of smoke will indicate leaks. Leaking joints are made good and the air test applied to test for soundness.

To test the performance of a discharge-pipe system in use, a group or groups of appliances are discharged simultaneously to cause conditions most likely to produce maximum pressure fluctuations. In buildings with up to nine appliances of each kind to a stack, the top-floor sink and wash basin are filled to overflowing and the plugs pulled simultaneous to a normal discharge of the top-floor W.C. After this test a minimum of 25-mm water seal should be retained in every trap. With more than nine appliances of each kind to a stack two or more W.C.s, basins and sinks are discharged simultaneously on the top floors for the performance in use test. The discharge from fittings to the top of a stack provides conditions most likely to cause pressure fluctuations sufficient to induce siphonage and back pressure and loss of water seal. In the performance in use test, the discharge from baths, showers and urinals is ignored as their use does not generally add significantly to peak flow conditions.

PIPE DUCTS

Since 1965 discharge stacks had to be run internally and it is usual in large modern buildings to run discharge pipework and cold- and hot-water services in ducts where possible. To economise in pipework and to avoid over large ducts it is necessary to group sanitary appliances. Some compact groupings of sanitary appliances and ducts and pipework are illustrated in Fig. 98, which illustrates ducts to a bathroom with W.C. and a separate bathroom and W.C.

Where there are two or more bathrooms and W.C.s on each floor of a multi-storey building, they will be grouped around a common duct as handed, left and right, side by side where there are two and handed and back to back to a single duct, where there are four.

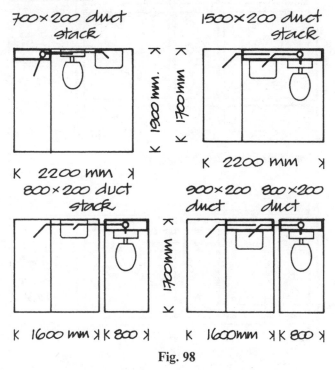

Fig. 98

VENTILATION OF INTERNAL W.C.s AND BATHROOMS

Bathrooms and W.C.s are often sited internally in modern buildings for freedom and economy of layout of rooms. It is necessary to provide means of ventilation to internal bathrooms and W.C.s by ducts to the open air to encourage air movement either by natural or mechanical ventilation.

Natural ventilation of internal rooms depends on wind pressure and the stack effect, which is the movement of heated air up a building or shaft. Natural ventilation is possible in low-rise buildings where high-level horizontal ducts to the open air will provide means of air change to ventilate internal rooms as illustrated in Fig. 99. It will be seen that a high-level duct allows air from the room to circulate to the open air, and replacement air from a lobby to enter, to provide adequate air change for ventilation. Obviously the successful operation of this system depends on wind speed and wind pressure. The system generally performs adequately in low-rise buildings of up to four or five floors.

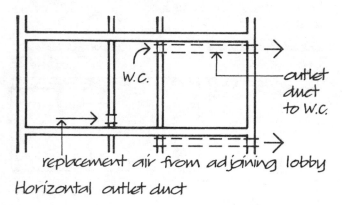

Horizontal outlet duct

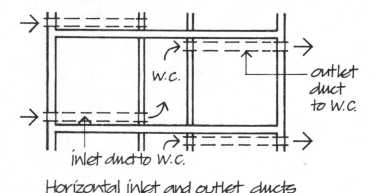

Horizontal inlet and outlet ducts

Fig. 99

The Building Regulations 1985 require natural ventilation to sanitary accommodation and bathrooms equal to at least $\frac{1}{20}$th of the floor area of the room, through a window, hinged Louvre panel, adjustable Louvre, airbrick or progressively openable ventilator which opens directly to open air.

In multi-storey buildings where sanitary accommodation and bathrooms are often grouped internally, it is a requirement of the Building Regulations 1985 that they be provided with mechanical ventilation capable of producing three air changes an hour.

Mechanical ventilation through a vertical duct is used to provide steady air changes independent of wind direction and pressure. Air is drawn through a common vertical duct to the outside air with branches to individual internal rooms as illustrated in Fig. 100. It will be seen that a main fan and duplicate stand-by fan at roof level, evacuate air through the vertical duct and shunt ducts to rooms. Replacement air enters the internal rooms from adjoining lobbies.

As an alternative the mechanical ventilation of sanitary accommodation and bathrooms may be intermittent, providing it runs for at least 15 minutes after the use of the room or space has stopped. This requirement is met by the use of an extractor fan, connected to the light switch so that the fan operates for 15 minutes after the light is turned off.

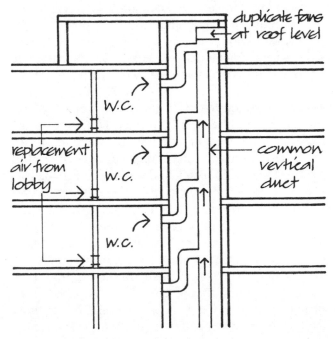

Mechanical extract system. Common duct with branches at each floor level

Fig. 100

CHAPTER FOUR

FOUL DRAINAGE

History: Short cylindrical vitrified clay pipes have for centuries been used for drains underground. The joints between the pipes were made with puddled clay, either packed around the butt ends of adjacent pipes, packed into loose clay collars joining pipe lengths or packed into the socket end of one pipe around the spigot end of the next. Puddled clay is plastic clay either in its natural wet state or to which water is added to make it plastic so that it can be moulded around or packed tightly into collars or sockets of pipes. A gaskin of hemp, usually tarred or coated with tallow was first rammed into the collars or sockets to align the pipes and prevent the puddled clay entering the pipeline. The clay pipeline was laid on the bed of a trench with a shallow fall towards the drain outflow and the trench then backfilled with the excavated material.

Well burnt (vitrified) clay or stoneware pipes were inert to sewage and impermeable to the intrusion of ground water and the puddled clay joints might remain watertight for many years, particularly in damp soil conditions. The plasticity of the clay joint would take up slight movements in the pipeline due to settlement, elongation or contraction of the pipeline and slight displacement of the pipeline caused by back-filling the pipe trench and pressure on the ground from above.

The small movements that the puddled clay joints could accommodate might allow some seepage of sewage water through the joints in the pipeline or intrusion of ground water into the pipe. The pipeline was buried underground, and unless considerable leaks from, or blockages of the pipeline demanded attention, it remained so.

Up to the middle of the nineteenth century, standards of hygiene were appreciably less than those of today. The common practice in towns was to drain sewage into cesspits (pits dug into the ground, near to and sometimes under buildings) which retained solids and released liquids into open ditches and rivers causing an all-pervading odour.

Following serious epidemics of typhus in the early nineteenth century, due to gross pollution of drinking water by sewage, there was a demand for drastic and rapid improvement in hygiene. During the latter part of the nineteenth century there was great activity in the building of new enclosed sewers to replace cesspits and an overall improvement in drain laying and maintenance.

By the beginning of the twentieth century the new wonder material, Portland cement, was being manufactured in quantity and the cement joint for drains and later the concrete bed were adopted, as a 'cure-all' for all time, for blocked or leaking drains. The notion was to make a dense rigid joint of cement and sand between the brittle (rigid) clay pipes with a view to a rigid pipeline that would remain tight to seepage from inside and infiltration of ground water from without. To make doubly certain, the rigidly jointed clay pipeline that was initially laid on the bed of a drain trench was later laid on a rigid concrete base laid in the trench bottom. This combination of rigidly jointed clay pipes on a solid concrete bed was accepted as sound drain-laying practice from the beginning to the middle of the twentieth century.

A vitrified cylindrical drain pipe is brittle or rigid and will, under load, crack. The great advantage of the clay pipeline with puddled clay joints was that although the short lengths of pipe could not in themselves accommodate movement, the very many plastic puddled clay joints could and did so without excessive seepage from or infiltration of ground water into the joints.

The movements that a pipeline underground may suffer are ground settlement, movement due to gain or loss of water in clay soils, disturbances during backfilling of the pipe trench and elongation or contraction due to temperature or moisture changes in the pipes and joints.

After the war (1939–45) the Building Research Station began an investigation of drain failures that culminated in Digests 124 and 125 (first series). The principal failures that were reported were due to blockage of the drain or excessive seepage from the drain requiring the attention of a builder.

At that time the two materials most in use for drain pipes were the traditional salt-glazed clay and the recently introduced pitch fibre. The investigations established that drain failures were due, in clay pipelines, to misalignment of the pipes, brittle fracture of the pipes or fracture of the rigid cement joint and in pitch fibre lines to flattening of the pipe or fracture of the joint coupling. These failures were caused by earth movement under or around the pipeline, or load stress on the pipeline from backfilling the trench, or surcharge loads on the ground above the trench, these causes often being made worse by supports placed under pipes during laying to facilitate alignment. Other causes of failure were temperature and moisture changes in the pipeline, often after laying and before backfilling the trench and also damage to pipes during handling.

Clay pipes generally failed by brittle fracture either across or along the pipe or around sockets whereas pitch fibre pipes generally failed by being flattened without fracture. The different behaviour of clay and pitch fibre pipes under load prompted the current classification of pipes as rigid and flexible. Rigid pipes are those that fail by brittle fracture before they suffer appreciable deformation and in this are included clay, concrete, asbestos cement and cast iron. Flexible pipes are those that suffer appreciable deformation before they fracture and these include pitch fibre and uPVC.

Very many of the failures of clay drainlines were a consequence of the rigidity of the pipes, the cement joints and the concrete bed in use at the time of the investigation. The rigidity of the pipeline and its bed were incapable of accommodating, without fracture, the soil movements and load stresses that a pipeline may well suffer. From this understanding of failures there developed the discontinuous concrete or granular bed, and the flexible jointing system of clay drainlines. Thus practice had gone full circle from the flexible puddled clay joint, through rigid cement joints and bed, back to the flexible joint and granular bed of today. The deformation of flexible pipes has been controlled by the use of a granular bed and limitations of load by the design of the trench and its backfilling.

The Approved Documents H1 of the Building Regulations 1985 provides practical guidance to meeting the requirements of the Regulations for foul drains. Recommendations for drains include layout, gradient, pipe size, materials and depth, granular bedding and back filling for drains.

Drainage layout: The layout of foul drains depends on whether foul water and rainwater are discharged to a common drain system or to separate drain systems, which in turn depends on whether there is one sewer carrying both foul and rainwater or separate sewers for foul and rainwater.

In many of the older urban areas of England there is one sewer that takes the discharge of both foul water and rainwater from roofs and paved areas. Foul water is the discharge from W.C.s bidets, baths, basins and sinks and rainwater the discharge of the run off of rainwater from roofs and paved areas.

When the single, combined sewers of the older urban areas were laid out there was, at best, only rudimentary filtration and treatment of the discharge from sewers to sea, river or inland soakaways. With later, more stringent controls for the purification of foul water, to minimise contamination of drinking water, it became convenient and economic to separate foul and rainwater discharges to reduce the volume of water discharged to foul water sewers and the necessary size of water purification plants.

Outside the older urban areas it is usual for foul water and rainwater to drain to separate drainage and sewer discharge systems. Practice, therefore, is for combined drainage and sewer systems in the older urban areas and separate foul and rainwater systems in all other areas.

A combined drainage system which carries both foul and rainwater has to be ventilated throughout to prevent foul air discharge to the open air. In this system it is necessary, therefore, to fit trapped gullies, with a water seal, to collect rainwater from roofs and paved areas. With separate systems of foul and rainwater drains it is only necessary to fit trapped gullies to the discharge of foul water fittings, where the discharge pipe does not serve as a ventilation pipe.

Fig. 101 is an illustration of combined and separate drainage systems to a small two floor house. As the drains for foul water and rainwater will generally run across each other at some point, it is necessary to adjust the level or gradient (slope) of the drains to accommodate this.

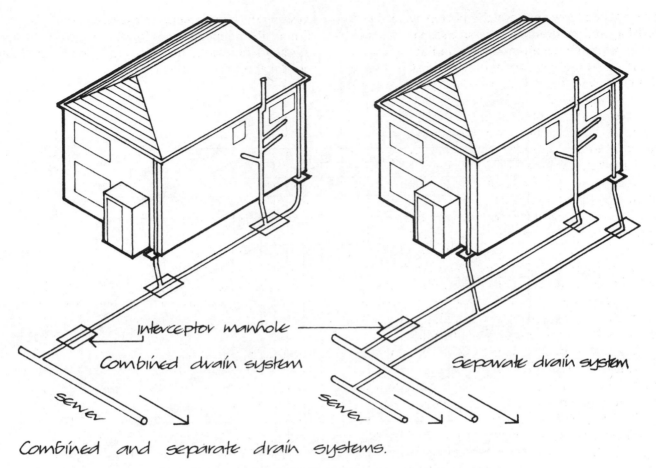

Combined and separate drain systems.

Fig. 101

Layout generally: For economy in the use of labour and materials, the layout of a drain system should be kept simple. To this end fittings that discharge foul water should be grouped together on each floor to economise in water service pipe runs and discharge pipe branches to a common waste stack and groups of fittings on each floor one over the other to avoid wasteful runs of pipework. Single fittings, such as basins or sinks, fitted distant from other fittings involve uneconomic and often unsightly lengths of water and discharge pipes.

Rainwater pipes from roof gutters and gullies to collect water from paved areas should be positioned to economise in and simplify drain runs.

Wherever practicable, changes of direction and gradient should be as few and as easy as possible to minimise access points necessary to clear blockages.

Foul water drainage systems should be ventilated by a flow of air with a ventilating pipe to the head of each main drain and any branch drain that is more than 10 metres long. Ventilated discharge pipes such as discharge stacks, discharging directly to the drain, are commonly used for ventilation of drains.

Drain runs should be laid in straight lines wherever possible to encourage the free flow of discharge water by gravity, with gentle curves in drain runs only where straight runs are not practicable. Bends in drain runs should be limited to positions close to or inside inspection chambers and to the foot of discharge pipes and should have as large a radius as practicable.

Where drain runs are near to or under a building, precautions should be taken to accommodate the effects of settlement without damage to the drain.

Pipe gradient (fall), pipe size: Up to about twenty years ago traditional wisdom was to use a 4 inch drain for up to four houses and a 6-inch drain for

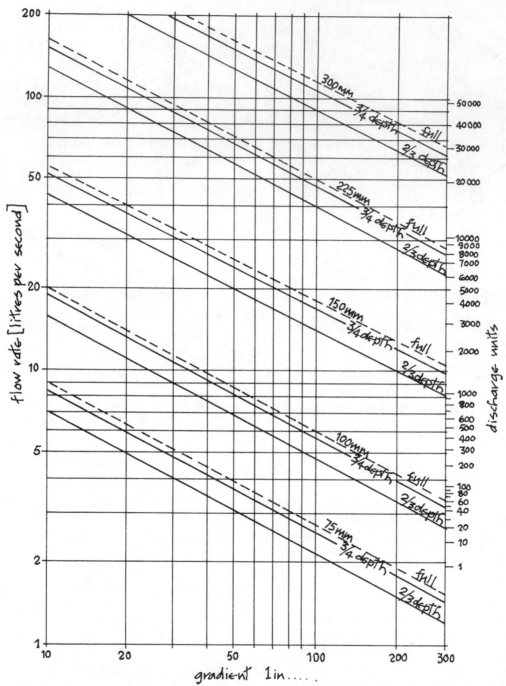

Discharge capacities of drains running full, ¾ and ⅔ proportional depth for used pipes in good condition.

Fig. 102

more than four houses the four inch drain being laid at a uniform gradient of 1:40 and the six inch drain at a gradient of 1:60. The gradient of the drain was related directly to the size of the pipe and bore little relation to the anticipated flow in the drain. The result was that drain pipes were often over sized and the gradient steeper than need be, resulting in excessive excavation.

Study of the flow load of drains in use has shown that the size of the drain pipe and its gradient should be related to the anticipated flow load. Estimates of the frequency of use of sanitary appliances have been used to determine discharge units. Discharge units for domestic appliances are 7 units for a 9-litre W.C., 6 units for a sink, 1 unit for wash basin and 7 units for a bath. As most domestic sanitary installations are in groups around a discharge stack, it is convenient to give a group discharge unit of 14, for a group of one 9 litre W.C., a bath, one or two basins and a sink. The discharge units represent flow load in a drain and correspond to rates of flow so that the discharge entering a drain will determine the necessary size and gradient of the drain.

Where the sanitary appliances from a few houses or flats discharge to a drain, the flow figures are so small as to require the smallest drain.

The graph in Fig. 102 is used to determine the required size of drain and its maximum and minimum gradient related to discharge units or flow in litres per second. The cumulative effect of discharges at discharge points down the length of a drain will affect the size and gradient of the drain.

Drains are designed to collect and discharge foul and rainwater by the flow of water under gravity. Drains are, therefore, laid to a regular fall (slope) towards the sewer or outflow. The necessary least gradient or fall of a drain depends on the anticipated flow of water through it and the necessary size of drain to carry that flow. Table 7 gives recommended minimum gradients for foul drains.

In Approved Document H1 of the Building Regulations 1985 is a recommendation that a drain carrying only waste water should have a diameter of at least 75-mm and that carrying soil water at least 100-mm. The term waste water is generally used to include the discharge from baths, basins and sinks and soil water the discharge from W.C.s.

Table 8, from Approved Document H1 of the Building Regulations 1985, shows the relationship of flow rate to gradient for three pipe sizes with drains

Table 7. Recommended minimum gradients for foul drains

Peak flow [litres/sec]	Pipe size [mm]	Minimum gradient [1:...]	Maximum capacity [litres/sec]
<1	75	1:40	4.1
	100	1:40	9.2
>1	75	1:80	2.8
	100	1:80*	6.3
	150	1:150†	15.0

Notes
* Minimum of 1 wc.
† Minimum of 5 wcs.

running three quarters of proportional depth. The rate of flow in drains with gradients as flat as one in two hundred is given in Table 8. Drains are not commonly run with gradients below one in eighty because the degree of accuracy necessary in setting out and laying drains required for shallow falls is beyond the skills of most building contractors.

Table 8. Discharge capacities of foul drains running 0.75 proportional depth

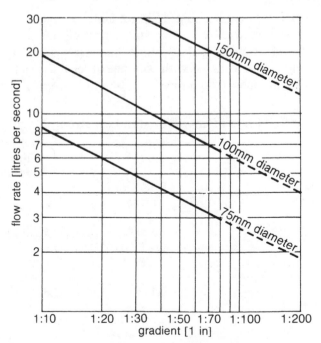

Depth of pipe cover: Drains should be laid at a depth sufficient to provide cover for their protection and the excavation should be as narrow as practical for bedding and laying the drain lines. The greater the width of the trenches at the crown of the pipe the greater the surcharge loads on the pipe. It is advantageous, therefore, to bed the drain in a narrow trench which may be increased in width above the level of the crown of the drain for ease of working. With modern excavating machinery flexible joint pipelines may be assembled above ground and then lowered into and bedded in comparatively narrow trenches so saving labour and cost in excavation and providing the best conditions for the least loads on the pipeline.

The depth of the cover to drain pipes depends on the depth at which connections are made to the drain, the gradient at which the pipes are laid and ground levels. Depth of cover is taken as the level of finished ground or paving above the top of a drain pipe.

A minimum depth of cover is necessary to provide protection to the pipe against damage and a maximum depth to avoid damage to the drain by the weight of the backfilling of the drain trenches. Minimum and maximum cover for rigid pipes is set out in Table 9.

Flexible pipes should have a minimum of 0.6 metres of cover under fields and gardens and 0.9 metres under roads.

Rigid pipes of less than 150-mm diameter with less than 0.3 metres of cover and pipes of 150-mm diameter or more, with less than 0.6 metres of cover should be surrounded with concrete at least as thick as the diameter of the pipe or 150 (whichever is the

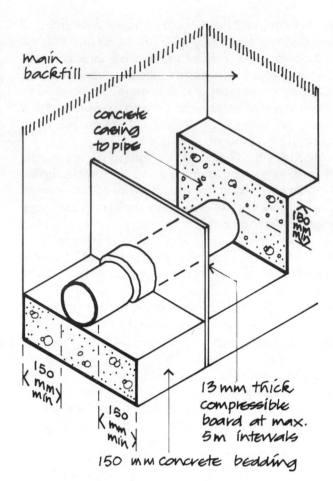

Concrete casing to rigid pipes

Fig. 103

Table 9. Limits of cover for standard strength rigid pipes in any width of trench

Pipe bore	Bedding class	Fields and gardens		Light traffic roads		Heavy traffic roads	
		Min	Max	Min	Max	Min	Max
100	D or N	0.4	4.2	0.7	4.1	0.7	3.7
	F	0.3	5.8	0.5	5.8	0.5	5.5
	B	0.3	7.4	0.4	7.4	0.4	7.2
150	D or N	0.6	2.7	1.1	2.5	–	–
	F	0.6	3.9	0.7	3.8	0.7	3.3
	B	0.6	5.0	0.6	5.0	0.6	4.6

greater) and with joints at not more than 5 metre intervals, as illustrated in Fig. 103.

Flexible pipes with less than 0.6 metres of cover under fields and gardens should be surrounded with concrete as described for rigid pipes or alternatively surrounded with granular fill and protected with a concrete paving slab as illustrated in Fig. 104.

Drains under or close to buildings: To allow for settlement, drain pipes run under a building should be surrounded with at least 100 of granular or other flexible filling and where the drain runs through a wall or foundation, an opening should be formed in the wall to provide 50 clearance all round as illustrated in Fig. 105, or alternatively a short length

of pipe, as short as possible, may be built into the wall with rocker pipes each side as illustrated in Fig. 105.

Where there is no choice but to run a drain close to a building, the drain trench should be filled with concrete as illustrated in Fig. 106, to avoid the damaging effect of settlement.

Bedding and backfilling: The recommendations in Approved Document H1 of the Building Regulations 1985 are that drain pipes be generally laid on some granular material such as natural aggregates, to a thickness of 100-mm below the pipes. This granular bed, which can be spread in the bed of the trench and levelled to the gradient or fall of the drain and scooped out to take the collars of pipes, provides a firm but flexible bed for drain runs. Once the drain lines have been laid and tested the drain trench is backfilled with granular fill or selected fill and then selected fill as illustrated in Figs 107, 108 and 109, for

granular fill as surround to drain pipes

concrete paving slabs laid on granular fill

main backfill over paving slabs

minimum 75 mm granular filling

flexible drain pipe

100 mm granular bedding

Protection for flexible pipes with less than 0.6 m. of cover under fields and gardens

Fig. 104

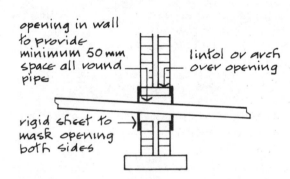

opening in wall to provide minimum 50 mm space all round pipe

lintol or arch over opening

rigid sheet to mask opening both sides

Drain pipe through opening in wall

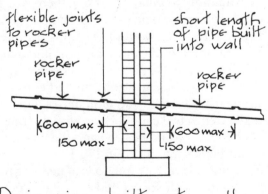

flexible joints to rocker pipes

short length of pipe built into wall

rocker pipe

rocker pipe

600 max
150 max

600 max
150 max

Drain pipe built into wall

Fig. 105

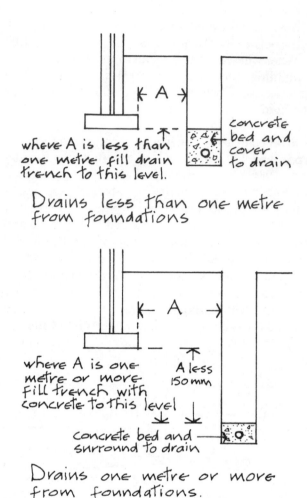

where A is less than one metre fill drain trench to this level.

concrete bed and cover to drain

Drains less than one metre from foundations

where A is one metre or more fill trench with concrete to this level

A less 150 mm

concrete bed and surround to drain

Drains one metre or more from foundations.

Fig. 106

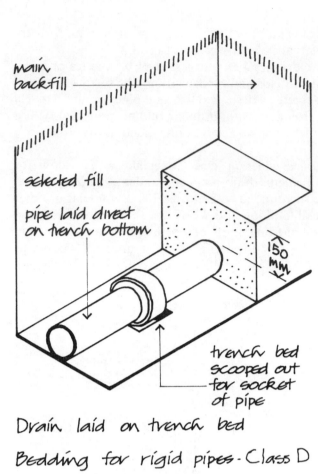

main backfill

selected fill

pipe laid direct on trench bottom

150 mm

trench bed scooped out for socket of pipe

Drain laid on trench bed

Bedding for rigid pipes · Class D

Fig. 107

rigid and flexible pipes. In Approved Document H1 of The Building Regulations 1985 there are four classes of bedding for rigid pipes. In Class D the pipes are laid on the trench bottom, which is trimmed to the gradient or fall of the drain pipes as illustrated in Fig. 107. This method of bedding is possible where a cohesive soil is sufficiently uniform and compact to be trimmed by hand to the gradient of pipe runs. Where the trench bed cannot be accurately trimmed, Class N bedding would be used and the pipe laid on a granular bed as illustrated in Fig 108.

Class F and Class B are methods of bedding for all soil conditions, with socket ends of pipe bedded in the granular bed of Class F and the bedding finished up to half the depth of pipes in Class B. The advantage of Class B bedding is that the bedding each side of the pipe will tend to retain the pipe runs

in correct line against disturbance that may be caused by subsequent backfilling.

The granular bedding for flexible pipes as illustrated in Fig. 109 is carried up to the crown of the pipe to give support to the pipe against deformation of the pipe under load. Any deformation of the pipe should be limited to 5% of the diameter of the pipe.

The advantage of the granular bedding is in the compactness and flexibility of the bedding to accommodate slight movements due to settlement, earth movement and movements due to temperature and moisture changes. The practical disadvantage of the granular bed is in the difficulty of bedding the whole of long pipe runs to a uniform gradient, directly on a coarse grained material as compared to the traditional method of supporting drain pipe joints on bricks or pads of wet concrete and then pouring a mix of wet concrete under and around the drain lines.

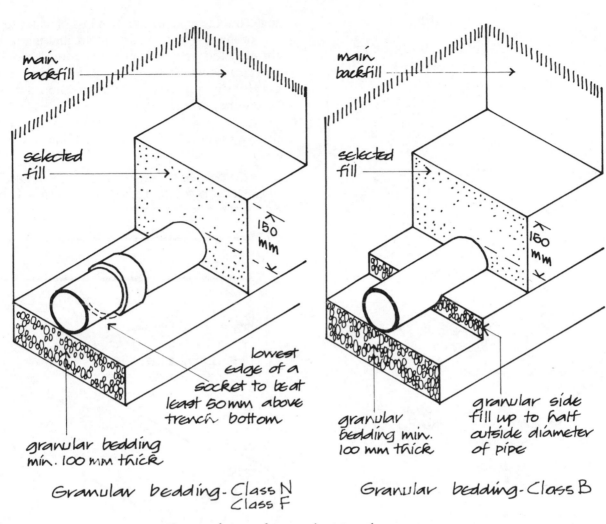

main backfill

selected fill

150 mm

lowest edge of a socket to be at least 50 mm above trench bottom

granular bedding min. 100 mm thick

Granular bedding - Class N Class F

main backfill

selected fill

150 mm

granular bedding min. 100 mm thick

granular side fill up to half outside diameter of pipe

Granular bedding - Class B

Bedding for rigid pipes

Fig. 108

DRAIN PIPES

Rigid pipes

Clay pipes, materials, manufacture, sizes: Up to the middle of the nineteenth century clay pipes were made from local clays and fired (burnt) in primitive kilns. Depending on the type of clay used, skill in moulding and the control of the firing, pipes varied from well-formed dense pipes to soft, porous, badly shaped pipes.

With the increase in urban population that followed the Industrial Revolution, and the demand from the middle of the nineteenth century for improvement in hygiene, came increase in the pro-

duction and quality of clay pipes. About this time it became common practice to use salt-glazed clay drain pipes – the clay pipe during firing being coated inside and out with a dense impermeable glaze. The fired-on salt-glaze coating rendered both dense and porous pipes alike impermeable to both infiltration and exfiltration of water.

More recently through quality control, preparation, moulding, drying and firing, clay pipes are produced which are sufficiently dense and impermeable in themselves so that they no longer require a salt glaze against exfiltration and infiltration of water. Old habits die hard however, and in spite of improved products and techniques the clay pipe

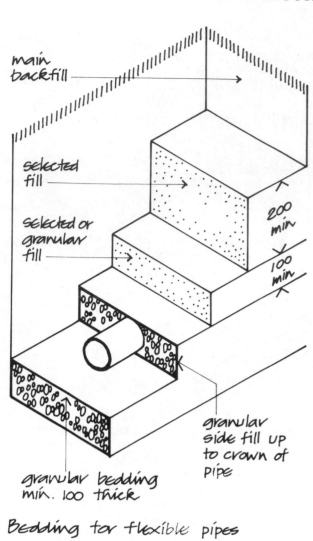

main backfill

selected fill

selected or granular fill

200 min

100 min

granular side fill up to crown of pipe

granular bedding min. 100 thick

Bedding for flexible pipes

Fig. 109

to encourage regular, uniform loss of water to avoid loss of shape. Pipes and fittings are automatically fed through and fired in continuous tunnel kilns. Pipes and fittings which are to be glazed have a ceramic glaze or slip sprayed on, or they are dipped in the slip before they enter the kiln.

The nominal bore (inside diameter) of clay pipes for drains is from 75 to 900 mm in increments of 25

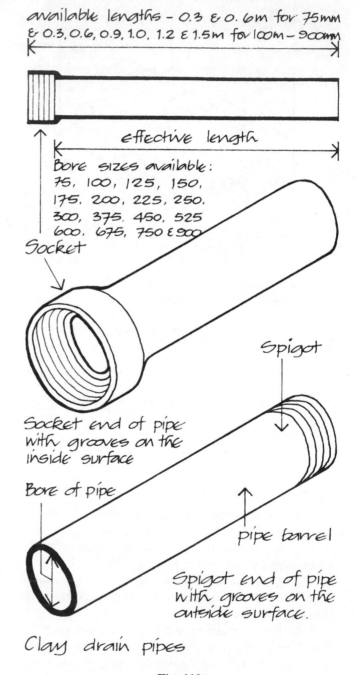

available lengths - 0.3 & 0.6m for 75mm & 0.3, 0.6, 0.9, 1.0, 1.2 & 1.5m for 100m – 900mm

effective length

Bore sizes available:
75, 100, 125, 150,
175, 200, 225, 250,
300, 375, 450, 525
600, 675, 750 & 900

Socket

Socket end of pipe with grooves on the inside surface

Bore of pipe

Spigot

pipe barrel

Spigot end of pipe with grooves on the outside surface.

Clay drain pipes

Fig. 110

manufacturers produce both vitrified clay pipes and vitrified clay pipes glazed either inside only, or both inside and outside to satisfy the demands of traditionalists, who claim without justification, that a glaze encourages flow in a pipe.

Today the majority of clay pipes are mass produced in a few highly automated plants. The selected clays are ground to a fine powder and just sufficient water is added for moulding. Pipes are formed by high-pressure extrusion, socketed pipes individually and plain pipes continuously, the cylinder of formed clay being cut to length. Straightforward fittings are formed by extrusion and the parts of junctions are extruded and then cut and joined by hand. The moulded clay pipes and fittings are then dried in kilns

between 75 and 250, one increment of 50 to 300 and increments of 75 from 300 to 900 as illustrated in Fig. 110. A very wide range of more than 250 fittings is made for clay drains such as bends, junctions, channels and gullies some of which are illustrated in Fig. 111.

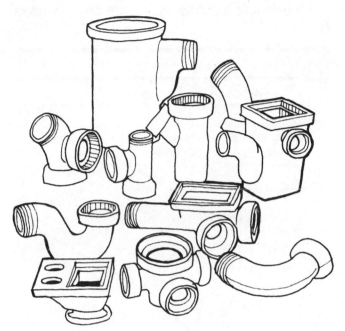

Clay drain pipe fittings

Fig. 111

The advantage of the clay pipe for drains is that the comparatively short length of pipe together with the wide range of fittings are adaptable both to the straight-forward and the more complex of drain layouts and the pipes themselves are inert to all normal effluents.

Jointing: It is now generally accepted that one of the flexible joints should be used with rigid clay drain pipes so that the drainlines are flexible in the many flexible joints. Flexible joints will accommodate earth movements under, around or over the pipeline. The flexible joint can be made in all weather conditions and once made and tested the trench can be backfilled to protect the pipeline from damage. There are two types of flexible joint in use: the socket joint for socket and spigot pipes and the sleeve joint for plain-ended clay pipes. Typical joints are illustrated in Figs. 112 and 113.

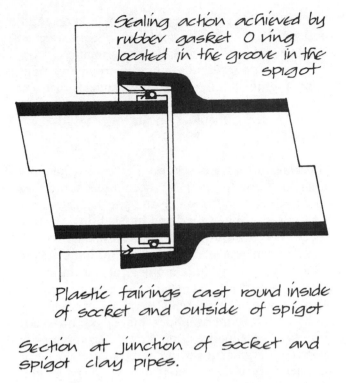

Sealing action achieved by rubber gasket O ring located in the groove in the spigot

Plastic fairings cast round inside of socket and outside of spigot

Section at junction of socket and spigot clay pipes.

Fig. 112

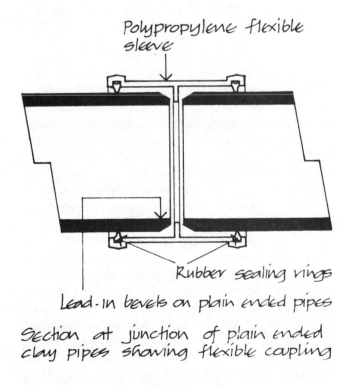

Polypropylene flexible sleeve

Rubber sealing rings

Lead-in bevels on plain ended pipes

Section at junction of plain ended clay pipes showing flexible coupling

Fig. 113

These flexible joints are made from either natural rubber, chloroprene rubber, butyl rubber or styrene-butadiene rubber. The flexible socket joint is cast on the spigot and socket ends of pipe to provide a simple push fit joint. It suffers the disadvantages that the joint may be damaged in handling and cut pipe lengths present difficulties on site.

Cast-iron pipes

Materials, manufacture, sizes: For over a hundred years cast-iron pipes have been used for drains underground and for water and gas mains. A cast-iron pipe is brittle or rigid and suffers brittle fracture under load. Cast iron has better resistance to corrosion than either steel or wrought iron. In its molten state it runs freely into moulds, producing good, sharp, plain or intricate shapes. A cast-iron pipe is stronger than the traditional clay pipe and has largely been used for drains under buildings and roads because of its superior strength. Cast-iron pipes are coated inside and out with a hot dip solution of tar or bitumen to protect the iron from sewage and ground water. Like other brittle or rigid pipes, cast iron may suffer brittle fracture under load or due to careless handling.

Some fifteen years ago ductile-iron pipes were first introduced. Molten grey iron (cast iron) is treated to change the micro-structure of the metal from the brittle graphite flake of cast iron to the ductile spheroidal graphite. The effect of this change is that the iron becomes ductile and can suffer deformation under load without fracture. The ductile-iron pipe is thus a flexible pipe having high tensile strength, ductility and resistance to severe impact without fracture.

Cast-iron pipes are used for drains because of their superior strength where there is unstable or made up ground, in shallow trenches, under buildings, for drains suspended under floors of buildings, in heavily waterlogged ground and where sewage is under pressure from pumping.

The traditional method of manufacturing cast-iron pipes is to pour molten grey iron into vertically mounted sand moulds. More recently, cast-iron pipes are made by spinning inside a mould. Molten grey iron is poured into a revolving water-cooled mould in which the molten metal forms on the inside of the mould by centrifugal force producing a pipe of even thickness and smooth finish. Casting by this method is rapid and continuous. Ductile-iron pipes

are also made by the spinmoulding process. Cast-iron and ductile-iron pipes are made with socket and spigot ends or with plain ends as illustrated in Fig. 114. All pipes are hot dip coated with either a bituminous or tar coating inside and out.

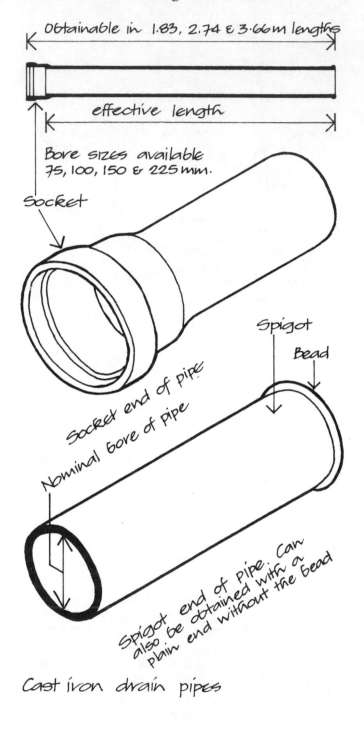

Cast iron drain pipes

Fig. 114

Pipes are manufactured with bore of 75, 100, 150 and 225 mm and in lengths of 1.83, 2.74 and 3.66 m, together with a wide range of fittings.

Jointing: The traditional joint for socket and spigot cast-iron pipes is the run lead or lead wool joint. A tarred jute gaskin is rammed (caulked) into the socket to align the pipes and prevent lead entering the pipeline. Molten lead is then run into the socket against an asbestos clip used to retain the molten lead in the joint. The cooled lead is then rammed into the joint as illustrated in Fig. 115. This is a skilled, laborious task that can only be carried out in dry weather, requires room for working and clean conditions all of which rarely combine in a drain trench. Lead wool, finely shredded lead, may be used in lieu of molten lead. The lead wool is hammered into the socket until it makes a watertight joint. This again is a laborious process.

A flexible push fit joint is commonly used today for cast-iron and ductile-iron pipes. A rubber gaskin, fitted inside the socket of pipes comprises a heel of hardened rubber that aligns the pipes and a bulb of softer rubber that makes the joint as illustrated in Fig. 116. The pipe ends must be clean and are lubricated and joined by leverage from a crowbar for small pipes, or a fork tool for larger pipes. The joint

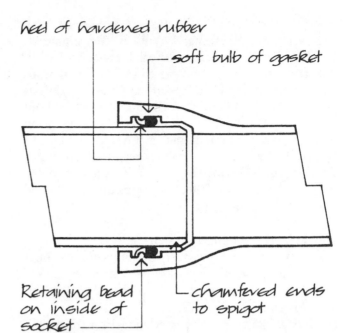

heel of hardened rubber

soft bulb of gasket

Retaining bead on inside of socket

chamfered ends to spigot

Flexible push fit joint for cast-iron

Fig. 116

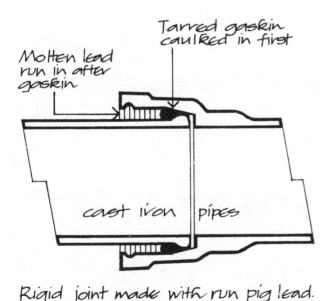

Tarred gaskin caulked in first

Molten lead run in after gaskin

cast iron pipes

Rigid joint made with run pig lead.

Fig. 115

is flexible and will accommodate longitudinal and axial movements. The joint is rapidly made in any conditions of weather, the pipeline may be tested right away and the trench backfilled to protect the pipeline.

Laying rigid pipes: The current recommended methods of laying rigid pipes on granular beds or on concrete and the methods of protecting pipes from damage by settlement or from loads on the surface have been described previously.

Flexible pipes
uPVC pipes
Materials, manufacture, sizes, bedding: uPVC pipes were first used for underground gas and water-pressure pipes some fifty years ago. This pipe material was first used in this country for underground drains some twenty years ago and is now very extensively used for its ease of handling, cutting, jointing and low cost. Polyvinyl Chloride (PVC) is made by the electrolysis of coal and chalk to form carbide. Water is added to form acetylene. Hydrochloric acid is then added to form the monomer of vinyl chloride. The monomer is polymerised to a fine white

powder of low density. To the PVC are added small quantities of lubricants, stabilisers and pigments. Heated uPVC material is extruded through a former and then 'frozen' by cooling to form a continuous pipe length. The pipe is light in weight and flexible as it can to some extent deform under load without fracture. Deformation should be limited to an increase in horizontal diameter of not more than 5% to avoid blockages in pipelines or breaks in joints. Pipe sizes are described by the outside diameter of the pipe as 110, 160 and 200 and lengths are 1.0, 3.0 and 6.0 m as illustrated in Fig. 117.

Jointing: Three jointing systems are used.
(1) Socket and spigot push fit joints with rubber sealing rings, the spigot either extruded integral with the pipe or as a separate coupling, as illustrated in Fig. 118.
(2) Sleeve joints of polypropylene with rubber sealing rings to plain-ended pipes as illustrated in Fig. 119.

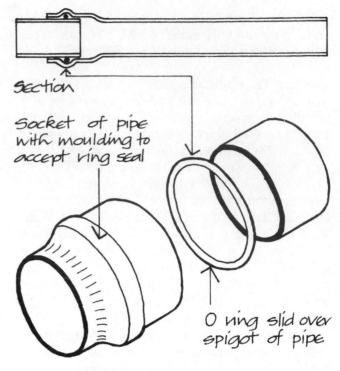

Section

Socket of pipe with moulding to accept ring seal

O ring slid over spigot of pipe

P.V.C. socket and spigot push fit joint.

Fig. 118

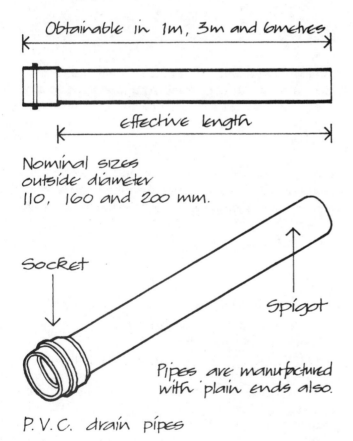

Obtainable in 1m, 3m and 6 metres

effective length

Nominal sizes
outside diameter
110, 160 and 200 mm.

Socket

Spigot

Pipes are manufactured with plain ends also.

P.V.C. drain pipes

Fig. 117

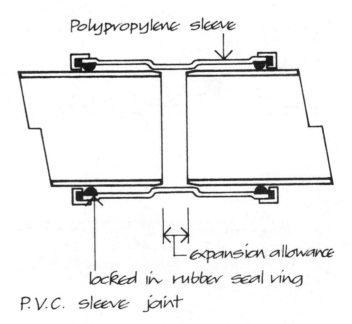

Polypropylene sleeve

expansion allowance

locked in rubber seal ring

P.V.C. sleeve joint

Fig. 119

(3) Solvent cement welding of spigot to socket joints as illustrated in Fig. 120.

Because of the comparatively long lengths in which this pipe material is made and consequent few joints necessary, the material lends itself to assembly at ground level from where it can be lowered into narrow trenches. This is a distinct advantage on most building sites.

uPVC drain pipes are commonly used with the proprietary drain systems such as the 'rodding eye' or the 'access bowl' drainage systems illustrated in Figs. 126 and 127. These systems comprise a package of plastic connections, clearing eyes and access bowls for inspection for economy and speed of assembly and laying.

Because of the comparatively extensive range of fittings manufactured in clay it is not uncommon for clay gullies, for example, to be used in conjunction with uPVC pipes.

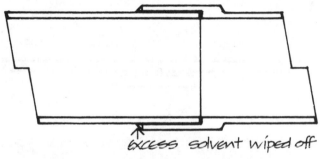

Pipe ends carefully cleaned before jointing

excess solvent wiped off

Welded joint achieved by bringing together spigot & socket of pipes which have been brushed at the ends with solvent — PVC solution and methyl chloride

P.V.C. solvent welded joint

Fig. 120

Pitch-fibre pipes
Materials, manufacture, sizes: Pitch-fibre pipes have been successfully used on the Continent and America for many years. They were first manufactured and used in this country from the middle of this century and were used for drains underground for both soil and surface water. The low cost, long length of pipe, ease of jointing together with the flexibility of the material recommend it as a drainpipe material.

The pipes are manufactured from a blend of wood cellulose products such as waste paper and other fibres. The fibres are mixed with water and woven into a felt of fibre-pipe size. The moulded fibre-felt pipe is then dried. The dried-fibre pipe is immersed in hot pitch and later in water to give the pitch-fibre pipe a gloss finish. Pitch-fibre pipes consist of about 30% of fibre and about 70% of pitch. The pipes have a nominal bore of 50, 75, 100, 125, 150, 200 and 225 and are supplied in lengths of 1.7, 2.5 and 3 m.

Jointing: The joints in use are as follows:

Taper coupling joint: This is the original joint when the pipes were first produced. The pipes have 2° tapered ends over which a 2° tapered coupling sleeve fits as illustrated in Fig. 121. The joint is made by driving the coupling together to close the joint.

Snap ring joint: A polypropylene coupling sleeve is used to join plain-ended pitch-fibre lengths, the joint being sealed by rubber 'D' section snap rings. The rubber rings are fitted around the ends of the pipes to be joined and the pipes pushed into the coupling sleeve. The rubber rings roll along the pipe ends until they snap close with the flat of the 'D' section rings bearing on the pipe.

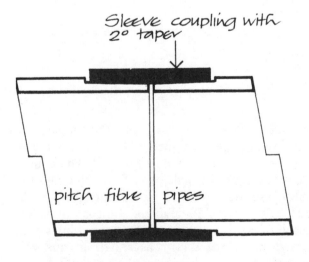

Sleeve coupling with 2° taper

pitch fibre pipes

2° taper coupling joint
Long Section through joint

Fig. 121

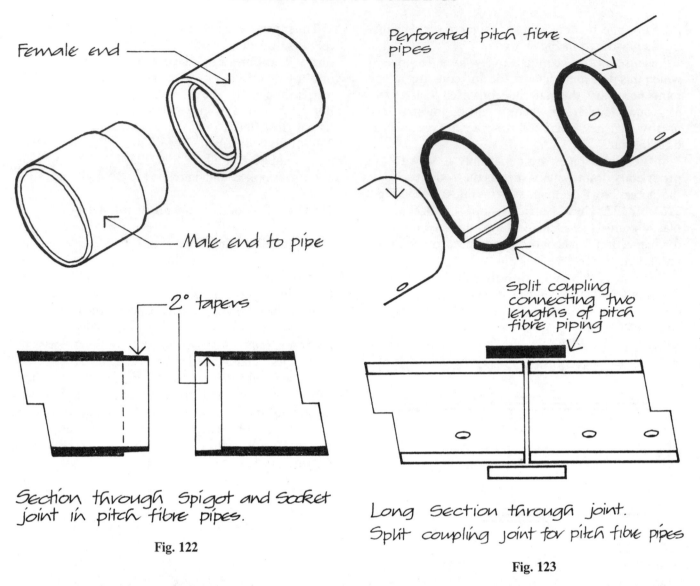

Female end

Male end to pipe

2° tapers

Section through Spigot and Socket joint in pitch fibre pipes.

Fig. 122

Perforated pitch fibre pipes

Split coupling connecting two lengths of pitch fibre piping

Long Section through joint. Split coupling joint for pitch fibre pipes

Fig. 123

Spigot and socket or rebated joint: The ends of the pitch-fibre pipe are machined with male and female rebated joints as illustrated in Fig. 122. The joint is made by pushing the male end of one pipe into the female end of the next. The joint locates the pipes in correct alignment. Although the joint is not watertight it is of no great consequence as this joint is used with perforated pipes serving as land drains and with plain pipes acting as conduits for electric cables.

Coupling joint: A split-coupling sleeve is used to join pitch-fibre pipes as illustrated in Fig. 123. This joint is used with perforated pipes for land drainage and plain pipes for electric conduit.

Pitch fibre pipes are much less used for drainage than they were some years ago principally because of the difficulty of making junctions and bends with the material and because of the very limited range of fittings. uPVC pipes have largely taken over as the principal flexible drain pipe material.

Pitch fibre pipes are still used for long straight runs of surface water and land drainage and as conduits for small cable and pipe material.

Laying flexible pipes: The current recommended methods of laying flexible pipes on granular beds and surrounds were described previously.

DRAINAGE SYSTEMS

Combined drain systems: Both foul and surface-water discharges to a common or combined drain system that in turn discharges to a combined public sewer. In the past great emphasis was placed on a system of water seals and vents designed to prevent sewer gases and odours entering buildings from drains and sewers. This unholy fear of drain smells has been taken to extreme and absurd limits that persist to the present day. With the high percentage consumption of water today and the mean rainfall in this country it is very unlikely that a combined drain flowing freely will cause objectionable smells. The very many water seals in the form of traps that are used against this slight possibility are in themselves expensive and a prime source of blockages.

In the combined drain system the discharge from sanitary pipework, rainwater pipework and surface water from paved areas runs to a common drainage system. For economy these three separate discharges should be run as directly as possible to a single drainline and the traditional method of achieving this is by means of an inspection chamber or manhole preferably outside the building as illustrated in Fig. 101. The chamber is so placed to collect the inlet pipes that discharge to the chamber in the direction of the flow of the drain.

Access points: Sufficient access points to drains should be provided to facilitate clearing blockages by the normal method of rodding.

The four types of access points in use are:

(1) Rodding eyes, which are capped extensions of drain pipes
(2) Access fittings, which are small chambers on or as an extension of drain pipes with no open channel
(3) Inspection chambers, which are large chambers with an open channel but not working space at drain level
(4) Manholes, which are large chambers with an open channel and working space at drain level

Access points should be provided on long drain runs and at or near the head of each drain run, at a bend or change of gradient, a change of pipe size and at junctions where each drain run to the junction cannot be cleared from an access point.

The limits of the depth and minimum dimensions for access points are set out in Table 10 and the minimum spacing of access points in Table 11.

Table 10. Minimum dimensions for access fittings and chambers

| Type | Depth to invert [m] | Internal sizes | | Cover sizes | |
		Length × width [mm × mm]	Circular [mm]	Length × width [mm × mm]	Circular [mm]
Rodding eye	—	As drain but min 100		—	
Access fitting small	0.6 or less	150 × 100	150	150 × 100	150
large		225 × 100	—	225 × 100	—
Inspection chamber	0.6 or less	—	190*	—	190*
	1.0 or less	450 × 450	450	450 × 450	450†
Manhole	1.5 or less	1200 × 750	1050	600 × 600	600
	over 1.5	1200 × 750	1200	600 × 600	600
Shaft	over 2.7	900 × 840	900	600 × 600	600

Notes
* Drains up to 150 mm.
† For clayware or plastics may be reduced to 430mm in order to provide support for cover and frame.

Table 11. Maximum spacing of access points in metres

From	To	Access Fitting Small	Large	Junction	Inspection chamber	Manhole
Start of external drain*		12	12	—	22	45
Rodding eye		22	22	22	45	45
Access fitting small 150 diam 150 × 100		—	—	12	22	22
large 225 × 100		—	—	22	45	45
Inspection chamber		22	45	22	45	45
Manhole		22	45	45	45	90

Note
* Connection from ground floor appliances or stack.

Inspection chamber – manhole: The traditional arrangement for inspecting, testing and clearing blockages in underground drains is the inspection chamber or manhole. This is a brick-lined pit at drain junctions and changes of direction or gradient in a drainline. The inspection chamber is located at those points where drain blockages are most likely to occur and from which blockages in drainlines can be cleared by rodding. The inspection chamber provides access to inspect flow in the drain and if necessary, means of testing drainlines. The traditional clay drain pipe was liable to blockages due to misalignment of the many joints or fracture of the pipes and their rigid cement joints and there was, therefore, advantage in constructing inspection chambers at fairly frequent intervals when labour costs were low.

Today, inspection chambers are comparatively costly items and with the increased length of pipes available and flexible joints that closely align pipes and accommodate slight movement, it is possible to use fewer inspection chambers. The suppliers of uPVC drain pipes utilise systems of rodding points or access bowls instead of inspection chambers for the purpose of clearing blockages. The rodding points cannot be used to inspect flow or for testing and it is usual to include one or more inspection chambers in this drain system.

The traditional inspection chamber or manhole is a brick-lined pit at the junction of drain branches, at changes of direction and gradient to facilitate inspection, testing and clearing obstructions; the chief purpose being access to clear blockages in any of the drain runs connecting inside the chamber. An inspection chamber is a small shallow chamber sufficient to clear blockages from above ground, and a manhole a deeper chamber large enough for a man to climb down into to clear blockages. An inspection chamber or manhole is formed on a 150 mm concrete bed, on which brick walls are raised. In the bed of the chamber a half-round channel or invert takes the discharge from the branch drains as illustrated in Fig. 124. The walls of the chamber may be of dense engineering bricks. If less dense bricks are used the chamber is lined with cement rendering inside to facilitate cleaning, and sometimes rendered outside to prevent the infiltration of ground water. The chamber is completed with a cast-iron cover and frame as illustrated.

The word invert is used to describe the lowest level of the inside of a channel in an inspection chamber, or the lowest point of the inside of a drain pipe, and measurements to the invert of a drain are used to determine the gradient of that drain. In the bed of the chamber the three-quarter section branch drains discharge over the channel in the direction of flow,

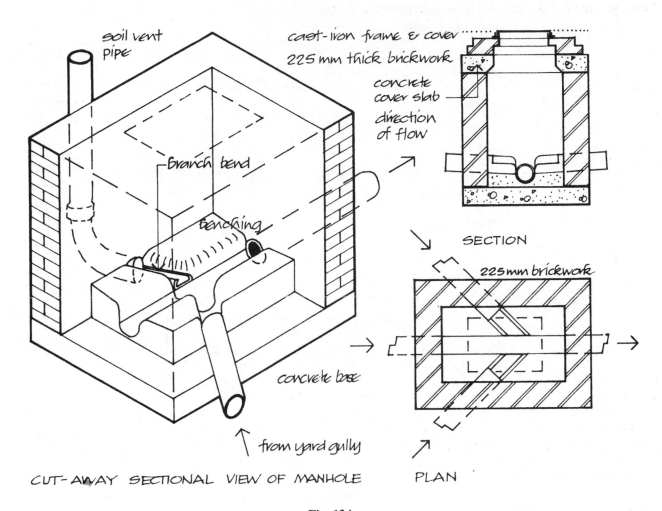

soil vent pipe

cast-iron frame & cover
225 mm thick brickwork
concrete cover slab
direction of flow

Branch bend

benching

concrete base

from yard gully

CUT-AWAY SECTIONAL VIEW OF MANHOLE

SECTION

225 mm brickwork

PLAN

Fig. 124

and fine concrete and cement rendering termed benching is formed around the branches to encourage flow in the direction of the fall of the drain as shown in Fig. 124.

Backdrop inspection chamber: Where a branch drain is to be connected to a main drain or a sewer at a lower level it is often economical to construct a backdrop inspection chamber to avoid deep excavation of a drainline. The backdrop chamber is constructed of brick on a concrete bed and the higher branch drain is connected to a vertical or drop drain that discharges to the channel in the backdrop chamber as illustrated in Fig. 125.

Rodding point drain system: This underground drain system combines the advantages of the long lengths of pipe and simplicity of jointing of uPVC drain lines with rodding points and one or more inspection chambers for access for inspection, testing and clearing blockages. Fig. 126 is an illustration of a typical layout. It will be seen that the rodding points are used as a continuation of straight drain runs extended to ground level with an access cap as illustrated in Fig. 126. It is possible to rod through each drain run to clear blockage and this arrangement dispenses with the need for inspection chambers at all junctions and bends with appreciable saving in cost. The drain runs are laid on granular bedding and backfilled as previously described.

91

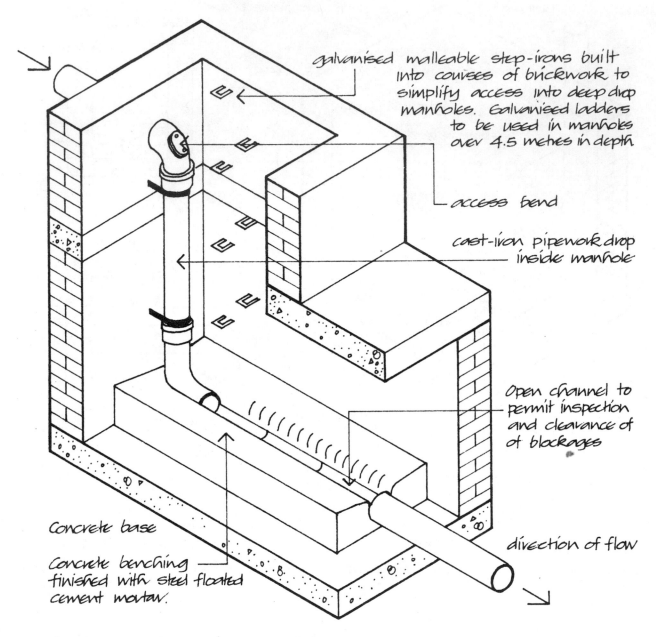

galvanised malleable step-irons built into courses of brickwork to simplify access into deep drop manholes. Galvanised ladders to be used in manholes over 4.5 metres in depth.

access bend

cast-iron pipework drop inside manhole

Open channel to permit inspection and clearance of of blockages

direction of flow

Concrete base

Concrete benching finished with steel floated cement mortar.

Back drop inspection manhole

Fig. 125

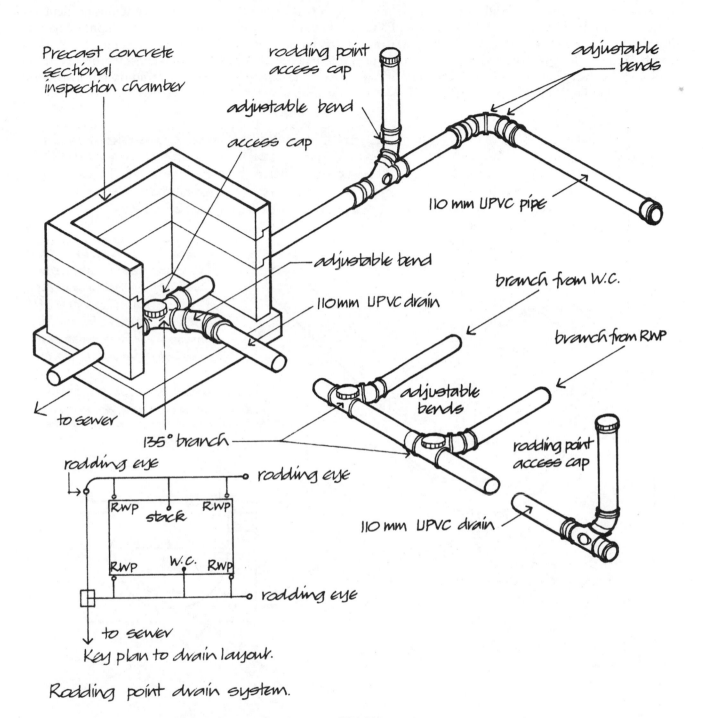

Precast concrete sectional inspection chamber

rodding point access cap

adjustable bends

adjustable bend

access cap

110 mm UPVC pipe

adjustable bend

110mm UPVC drain

branch from W.C.

branch from RWP

adjustable bends

to sewer

135° branch

rodding point access cap

110 mm UPVC drain

rodding eye

rodding eye

RWP   stack   RWP

RWP   W.C.   RWP

rodding eye

to sewer

Key plan to drain layout.

Rodding point drain system.

Fig. 126

Access bowl drain system: A shallow bowl collects the soil, waste, rainwater and surface-water discharges from buildings and discharges to uPVC drainlines. The bowls are at ground level with the length of the outlet pipe adjusted to the depth of the drainline below ground to minimise excavation down to the level of the drain. Fig. 127 is an illustration of a typical access bowl with branches and outlet to drain. This drain system is particularly suited to housing estates where the houses may be connected to a combined drain through access bowls as illustrated in Fig. 127, with considerable savings in cost as compared to the traditional inspection chamber and drainline systems.

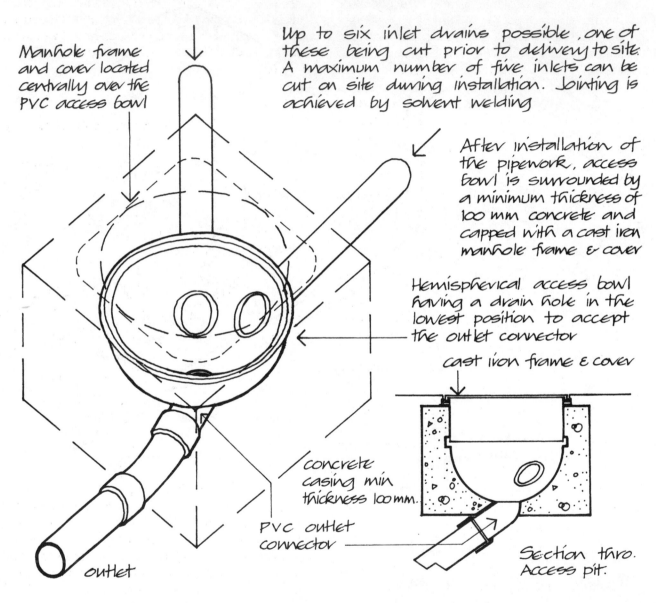

Manhole frame and cover located centrally over the PVC access bowl

Up to six inlet drains possible, one of these being cut prior to delivery to site. A maximum number of five inlets can be cut on site during installation. Jointing is achieved by solvent welding

After installation of the pipework, access bowl is surrounded by a minimum thickness of 100 mm concrete and capped with a cast iron manhole frame & cover

Hemispherical access bowl having a drain hole in the lowest position to accept the outlet connector

cast iron frame & cover

concrete casing min thickness 100mm.

PVC outlet connector

outlet

Section thro. Access pit.

Mascar access bowl drain system.

Fig. 127

Soil pipe connections to drains: From Fig. 124 it will be seen that the soil pipe connects directly to the inspection chamber and serves to ventilate the drain system. For this purpose the soil pipe is carried up above roofs. To obviate blockages the soil pipe should be connected to its drainline with an easy sweep bend as illustrated in Fig. 124. To facilitate clearing blockages there may also be an access trap.

Soil and waste pipes to buildings of more than three storeys are run inside buildings to prevent blockages by freezing and for ease of access to clear blockages. Where the drain connection to a soil or waste pipe passes through the wall of the building there must be at least 50 mm clearance all round the drain to accommodate differential movements between wall and drain that might otherwise fracture the drain as illustrated in Fig. 128.

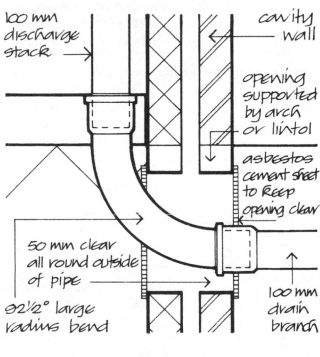

Fig. 128

Gullies: When there are separate soil and waste-discharge pipes that discharge separately to a combined drain, the waste water discharge pipe is connected to a back inlet gully, and the foul water discharge pipe discharges directly to the drain. The purpose of the gulley is to give access for clearing blockages and provide a water seal between the foul drains and the pipes above ground. Similarly rain-

water pipes discharge to gullies which as before provide a water seal, as illustrated in Fig. 129. Likewise yard gullies which collect surface water are provided with a water seal when they discharge to foul drains.

Where there are separate drain systems for foul water and rain and surface water, the rainwater discharge pipes and the yard gullies that collect surface water can be connected directly to the surface water drain, without trapped gullies, as there are no foul gases or air in the drain or sewer that may cause a smell.

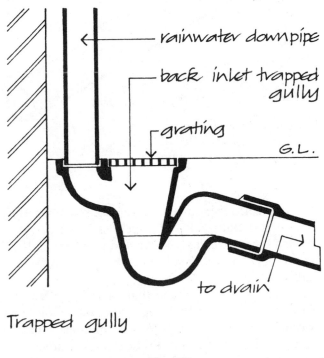

Trapped gully

Fig. 129

It will be seen from Fig. 130 that the gullies collecting both rainwater and surface water from paved areas do not have a water seal. As there is not the same likelihood of blockages in surface-water drains it is not considered necessary to form inspection chambers at all junctions, bends and changes of gradient as is the case with foul-water drains. Rodding eyes at salient points to facilitate clearing drains are generally considered adequate for the purpose.

Private sewers: Considerable economies in drainage may be effected by the use of combined drains or private sewers. There is no exact distinction between

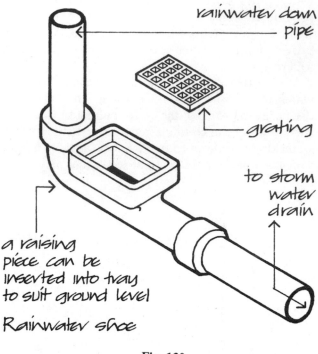

rainwater down pipe

grating

to storm water drain

a raising piece can be inserted into tray to suit ground level

Rainwater shoe

Fig. 130

Until comparatively recent times, it has been practice, in the older urban areas, to build an intercepting or disconnecting trap into the drainline connection to combined and foul water sewers. An intercepting trap is a water-sealed trap incorporating a rodding eye which is built into an intercepting chamber near the boundary of buildings in the out fall drain to sewers, as illustrated in Fig. 132. The purpose of the trap is to provide a water seal between

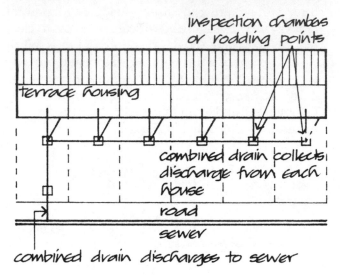

inspection chambers or rodding points

terrace housing

combined drain collects discharge from each house

road

sewer

combined drain discharges to sewer

the words drain and sewer, but the most generally accepted definition is that pipelines under privately owned land are called drains, and pipelines laid and maintained by the local authority under roads are called sewers.

A private sewer is one that takes the discharge from two or more buildings, runs under the land within the ownership of those buildings and discharges to the public sewer. The economic advantage of a private sewer is that it reduces drain runs from each building and the expense of individual connections to sewers as illustrated in Fig. 131. Where a private sewer is used to drain privately owned buildings it is necessary to apportion the cost of maintenance to the several users.

Connections to sewers – intercepting traps: Connections to public sewers are generally made by the local authority and paid for by the building owner or made by the building owner under the supervision of the local authority. In new development with new sewers a branch connection is constructed in the sewer and where there is an existing sewer the old sewer is broken into and a new saddle piece connection is made.

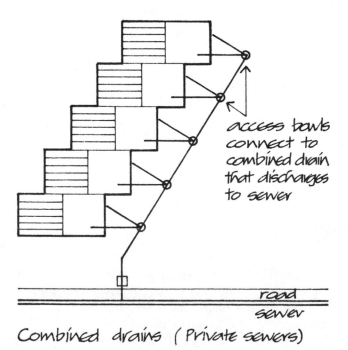

access bowls connect to combined drain that discharges to sewer

road

sewer

Combined drains (Private sewers)

Fig. 131

96

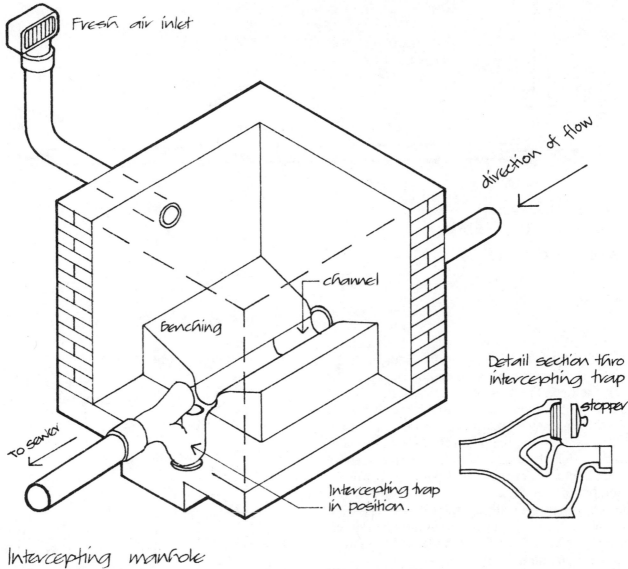

Fresh air inlet

direction of flow

channel

benching

Detail section thro
intercepting trap

stopper

To sewer

Intercepting trap
in position.

Intercepting manhole

Fig. 132

the sewer and the private drain against sewer gases rising into the private drains and hopefully as a bar against rats finding their way from the sewer into the private drain system. Because of this water seal, a ventilation pipe, termed a fresh-air inlet is connected to the inspection chamber to ventilate the private drain, as illustrated in Fig. 132. An intercepting trap is a prime cause of blockages in foul drains. It is no longer considered necessary to provide a seal between sewer and drains, and modern practice is to dispense with the intercepting trap and its inspection chamber and discharge the drain directly into the sewer.

DRAIN TESTING

Water test: All newly laid drainlines should be tested for watertightness after jointing and laying and again after backfilling and consolidation of trenches. As the object of testing is to ensure watertightness, the water test should be used. The drain is tested by water pressure applied by stopping the low end of the drain and filling it with water to a minimum head of water as illustrated in Fig. 133. The head of water should be 1.5 m above the crown of the high end of the pipeline under test. Where long drainlines are to be tested, and the head of water would exceed 6 m at

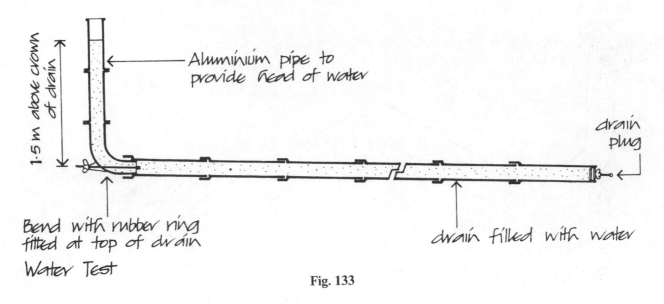

Aluminium pipe to provide head of water

1·5 m above crown of drain

Bend with rubber ring fitted at top of drain

Water Test

drain plug

drain filled with water

Fig. 133

the low end due to the length and gradient of the drain, it is necessary to test in two or more sections along the line. The loss of water over a period of thirty minutes should be measured by adding water from a measuring vessel at regular intervals of ten minutes, and noting the quantity required to maintain the original water level. The average quantity added should not exceed 1 litre per hour per linear metre, per metre of nominal internal diameter. The water test is a test of watertightness under pressure, a condition that a freely flowing drain will never suffer, and is thus a test of watertightness far more rigorous than the drainline is designed for.

Air test: The air test is generally accepted as a less rigorous test than the water test. The drainline to be tested is stoppered at both ends and air pressure is provided by a pump, the pressure being measured by a graduated 'U' tube or manometer, as illustrated in Fig. 134.

Smoke test: This test is used for old drains where the water or the air test is too rigorous for them to withstand. The drain to be tested is stoppered at suitable intervals and smoke is introduced under pressure from a smoke capsule or smoke machine. The purpose of the test is to discover leaks by the escape of smoke either when the line has been uncovered or is underground. An escape of smoke

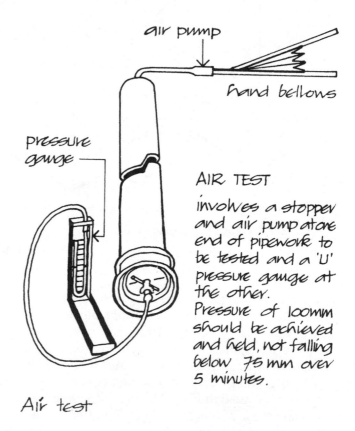

air pump

hand bellows

pressure gauge

AIR TEST

involves a stopper and air pump at one end of pipework to be tested and a 'U' pressure gauge at the other.
Pressure of 100mm should be achieved and held, not falling below 75 mm over 5 minutes.

Air test

Fig. 134

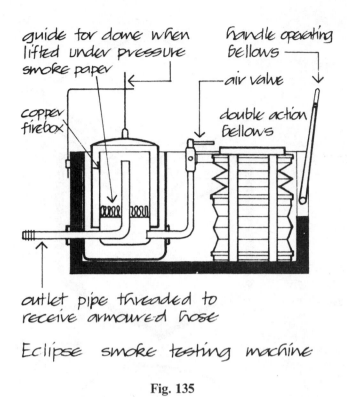

guide for dome when
lifted under pressure
smoke paper

handle operating
bellows

air valve

double action
bellows

copper
firebox

outlet pipe threaded to
receive armoured hose

Eclipse smoke testing machine

Fig. 135

will find its way to the surface through a considerable depth of soil and all but the most dense concrete cover. Fig. 135 illustrates a smoke test machine.

SOAKAWAYS, CESSPOOLS, SEPTIC TANKS

Soakaways: Where the subsoil is porous (pervious) and either the foul or surface-water sewer is some distance from the building or in outlying areas where there is no sewer it is convenient to construct soakaways to collect surface-water and rainwater discharges. A soakaway is a pit either unlined or lined into which the water is discharged and from which the water seeps or soaks away to the surrounding pervious subsoil.

Obviously if the soil is waterlogged and the water table or natural level of subsoil water is near the surface it is pointless to construct a soakaway. In this situation the surface water will have to be discharged by pipe to the nearest sewer, stream, river or pond.

In firm pervious ground such as chalk, it is generally sufficient to dig a pit into which the water is drained directly and the pit is covered with a concrete slab as illustrated in Fig. 136.

In moderately compact soils such as clay the pit may be filled with hardcore or clean broken stone to maintain the sides of the pit as illustrated in Fig. 136.

In granular soils such as gravel and sand the soakaway pit has to be lined with brick, stone or concrete to maintain the sides of the pit and the lining of brick stone or concrete must be porous or perforated to encourage the water to soak away into the surrounding soil as illustrated in Fig. 136.

It is often cheaper to excavate two or more small soakaways rather than one large one to reduce drain run lengths.

Soakaways should be at least three metres away from buildings so that the soakaway water does not affect the buildings' foundations, and should also be on slopes down from buildings rather than towards buildings to avoid overflowing and flooding.

Cesspools: A cesspool, sometimes termed a septic tank, is an underground chamber for the collection and storage of foul water. They are used for buildings in outlying areas where there is no nearby sewer. The underground cesspool should be watertight to loss of water from within and entry of ground water from without, the former to avoid ground pollution, the latter to prevent flooding and overflowing of the chamber.

Many local authorities provide a service of emptying cesspools on a regular basis, weekly or monthly, free of charge and more frequent collections on payment by the building owner. The authorities empty the cesspools by pumping to a tanker which then discharges the foul liquid to a sewage-treatment works.

Some local authorities require an overflow drain system to cesspools in the form of porous drains laid near the surface from which the overflow liquid leaks or soaks into the surrounding ground.

Cesspools may be lined with brick, block or concrete brick or block linings being rendered inside and surrounded with concrete outside. The cesspool is covered with a reinforced concrete slab in which is set a cover and a fresh air inlet.

Fig. 137 illustrates a typical cesspool construction.

Septic tanks – Small sewage-treatment plant An alternative to the use of a cesspool is a sewage-treatment plant. These small sewage-treatment plants comprise a septic tank and a filter bed.

The foul water is first drained to the septic tank,

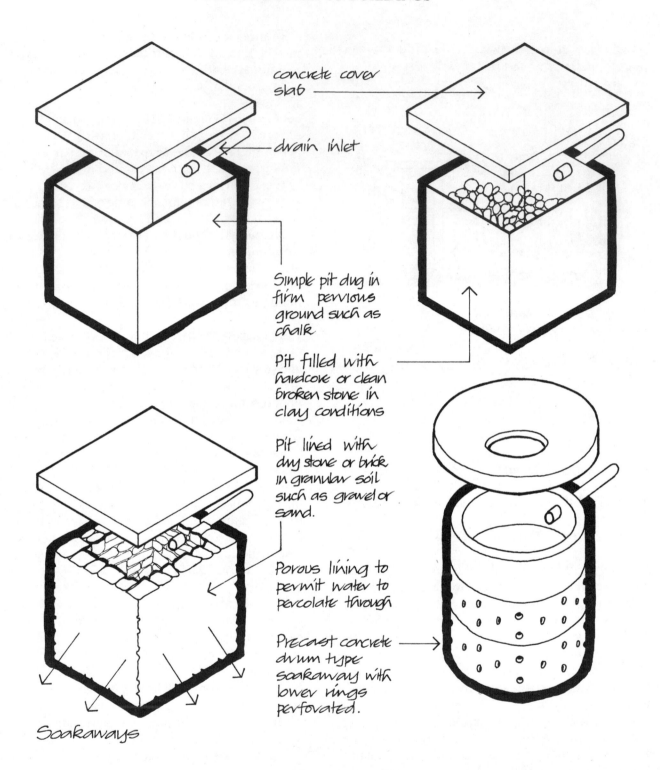

concrete cover slab

drain inlet

Simple pit dug in firm pervious ground such as chalk

Pit filled with hardcore or clean broken stone in clay conditions

Pit lined with dry stone or brick in granular soil such as gravel or sand.

Porous lining to permit water to percolate through

Precast concrete drum type soakaway with lower rings perforated.

Soakaways

Fig. 136

100

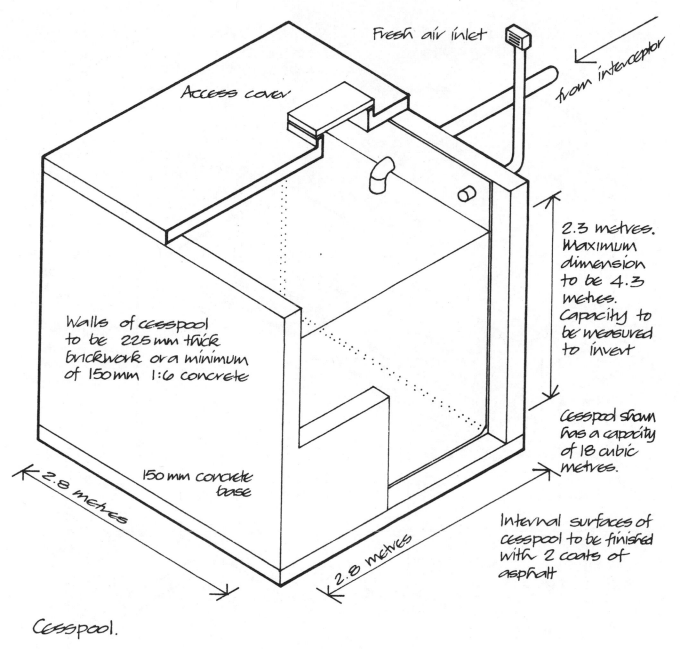

Fresh air inlet

from interceptor

Access cover

2.3 metres. Maximum dimension to be 4.3 metres. Capacity to be measured to invert

Walls of cesspool to be 225mm thick brickwork or a minimum of 150mm 1:6 concrete

Cesspool shown has a capacity of 18 cubic metres.

150 mm concrete base

2.8 metres

2.8 metres

Internal surfaces of cesspool to be finished with 2 coats of asphalt

Cesspool.

Fig. 137

usually large enough for forty-eight hours' flow, in which the solid organic matter is broken down by the action of anaerobic bacteria and in which the solid matter settles to the bed of the tank. A scum forms on the surface of this liquid in the septic tank as a consequence of the bacterial action. This scum is an effective seal between the liquid and the air in the tank.

In operation a septic tank is like a cesspool, as in both, solid matter settles to the bed of the chamber. The terms septic tank, cesspool and sedimentation tank or chamber are often interchanged.

The liquid from the septic tank drains to a filter bed designed to expose the liquid to as large an area of air as possible where the action of aerobic bacteria breaks down the residual organic compounds by

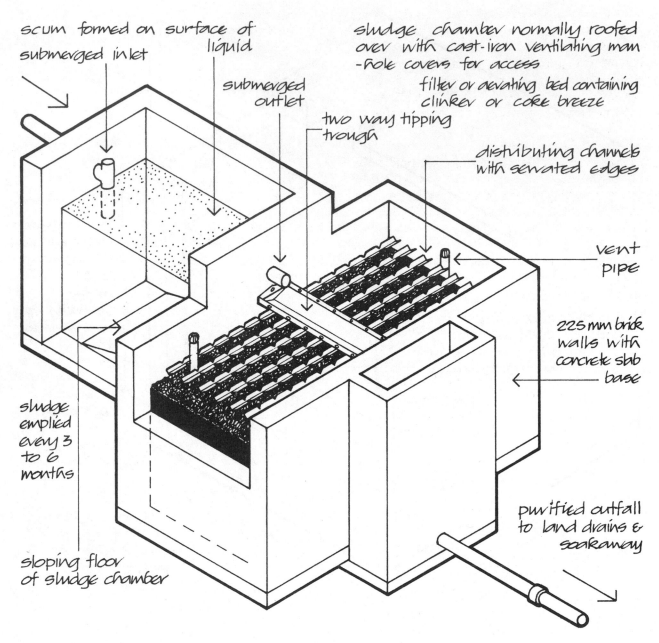

scum formed on surface of liquid submerged inlet

submerged outlet

sludge chamber normally roofed over with cast-iron ventilating man-hole covers for access

filter or aerating bed containing clinker or coke breeze

two way tipping trough

distributing channels with serrated edges

vent pipe

225 mm brick walls with concrete slab base

sludge emptied every 3 to 6 months

purified outfall to land drains & soakaway

sloping floor of sludge chamber

Septic tank suitable for isolated buildings

Fig. 138

oxidisation. The resulting purified liquid is then discharged to a stream or river or is drained to adjacent land. Fig. 138 is an illustration of the operation of a small sewage-treatment plant.

For efficient operation these sewage-treatment plants need regular attention. The sludge should be collected from the bed of the septic tank about every half year and may be carted away or used as fertiliser. The filter medium of the filter bed should be washed about once a year.

The sewage-treatment plant may be purpose-built with brick walls on a concrete bed as illustrated in Fig. 138 or from one of the pre-cast concrete, plastic or metal installations available.

Pumps. Where sanitary fittings and their drains are below the level of the sewer due to the slope of the ground or in basements it is necessary to raise the foul water by pumping. A sewage pump is an expensive piece of equipment and requires frequent maintenance if it is to function adequately. The need for pumping sewage should thus be avoided if at all possible.

The types of equipment used are the pneumatic ejector and the mechanical pump. The pneumatic ejector is used for small installations where the flow of sewage is small as for one or a few houses and where the sewage has to be raised comparatively small distances.

The pneumatic ejector is a relatively simple device with few moving parts to go wrong. The sewage enters the ejector cylinder through a non-return valve and raises a float that operates the air valves. Compressed air forces the sewage out through another non-return valve up to the sewer level and as the float falls the compressed air is evacuated. The ejector cylinder is fed by gravity from the drains. The air compressor and its air cylinder may be fitted adjacent to the ejector unit or at a higher level. The air compressor automatically operates to keep the air cylinder charged.

The operation of the pneumatic ejector is simple and straightforward and requires the least maintenance.

Where there is appreciable flow of sewage to be raised some distance to the sewer a mechanical pump system is used. The two systems used are the submersible pump and the dry well suction pump.

Submersible pump: Either the pump and motor unit is submersed in the foul sewage to be raised, or the pump is submersed with the motor raised as illustrated diagrammatically in Fig. 139. In either case maintenance of the submerged parts is a disagreeable task. The advantage of the submersible pump is that it operates more efficiently than a pump distant from the liquid to be pumped. Fig. 139 illustrates a submersible pump.

Dry-well suction pump: The pump is installed in a dry chamber or well adjacent to the well or chamber containing the sewage to be raised. The obvious advantage here is the relatively greater facility for inspection and maintenance. Fig 140 illustrates a typical system.

For continuous operation it is necessary to duplicate sewage-pumping systems.

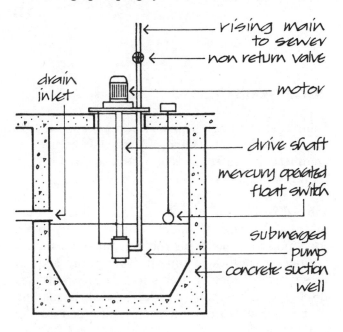

Submersible sewage pump

Fig. 139

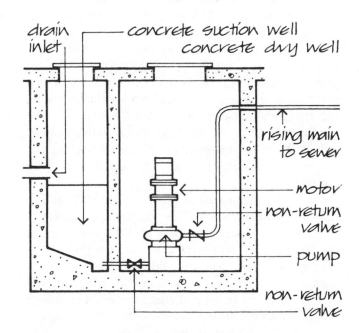

Dry well sewage pump

Fig. 140

CHAPTER FIVE

ROOF AND SURFACE WATER DRAINAGE

ROOF DRAINAGE

Rainwater running off pitched roofs is collected by eaves or valley gutters and off flat roofs by gutters, channels, rainwater heads or outlets, and discharged by rainwater pipes to drains.

Pitched roofs: The size of eaves and valley gutters and the spacing of outlets and rainwater pipes (downpipes) depend on the estimated maximum volume of rainwater run-off from roofs and an economical layout of drains to take the rainwater discharge. Eaves gutters collect rainwater running off pitched roof slopes and to make the best use of the gutter it is practice to fix the gutter to fall towards each side of an outlet to economise in gutter size and number of rainwater pipes as illustrated in Fig. 141. Obviously to drain a given roof, a large gutter will require fewer outlets and pipes than a small gutter as illustrated in Fig. 141. Which of these two arrangements shown is used will depend on economy in use of gutters and downpipes, economy of drain runs, position of windows and appearance. In the examples shown in Fig. 141 it would be possible to utilise two rainwater pipes, one at each end of the roof, with the gutter falling each way from the centre of the roof. Each half of the length of gutter would have to collect more rainwater than any one length of fall shown in Fig. 141 and a large gutter would be required.

Eaves gutters are usually fixed to a shallow fall of 1 in 360 towards outlets. This shallow fall avoids too large a gap between roof edge and the low point of the gutter, yet is sufficient to encourage flow in the gutter and allow for any slight settlement of the gutter.

Eaves gutters to hipped roofs are fixed to collect rainwater from all four slopes with angle fittings at corners as illustrated in Fig. 142, to allow water to run from the hipped end slope to the outlets to main slopes. In the illustration two downpipes are shown to each main roof slope with the gutter to the hipped

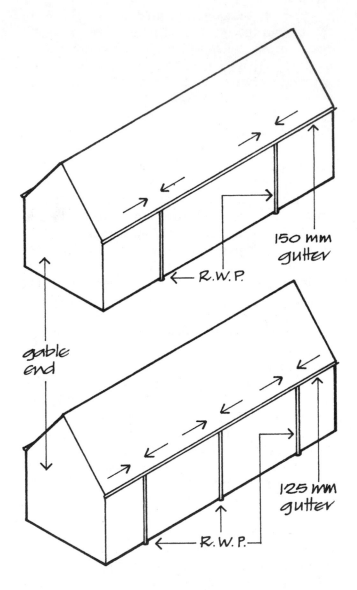

Gutters and downpipes

Fig. 141

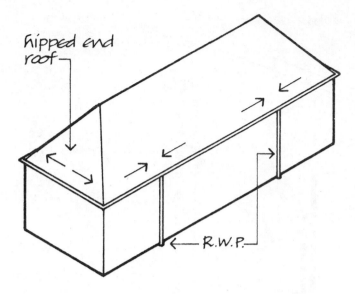

hipped end roof

R.W.P.

Hipped end roof

Fig. 142

Segmental gutter

Half round gutter

Ogee or O.G. gutter

Fig. 143

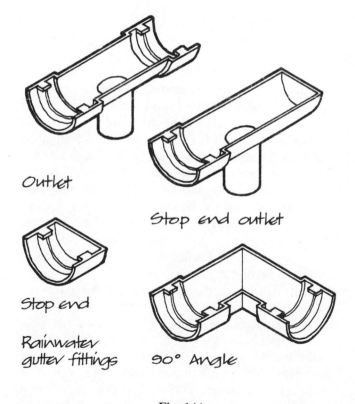

Outlet

Stop end outlet

Stop end

Rainwater
gutter fittings

90° Angle

Fig. 144

ends draining each way to the gutters to the main roof slopes. A square angle in a gutter, within 4 m of an outlet somewhat impedes flow, and allowance is made for this in the calculation of flow in gutters.

Eaves gutters for domestic and other small buildings are usually half round, segmental or ogee (O.G.) in section as shown in Fig. 143 and made of cast iron, pressed steel, aluminium, uPVC or sheet metal. Gutter lengths have socket and spigot ends, outlets, angle fittings and stop ends as illustrated in Fig. 144. The gutter outlet may be rounded or square cornered. Square-cornered outlets to gutters over 100 impede flow to an appreciable extent as illustrated in Fig. 145. for this reason some outlets are rounded as illustrated in Fig. 145.

Rainwater pipes are usually round section and of the same material as the gutter and have socket and spigot ends as illustrated in Fig. 146.

105

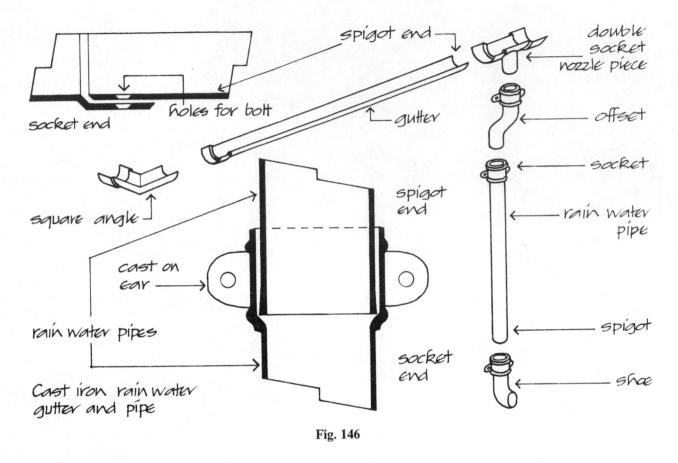

socket end

holes for bolt

spigot end

gutter

double socket nozzle piece

offset

socket

rain water pipe

square angle

cast on ear

rain water pipes

Cast iron rain water gutter and pipe

spigot end

socket end

spigot

shoe

Fig. 146

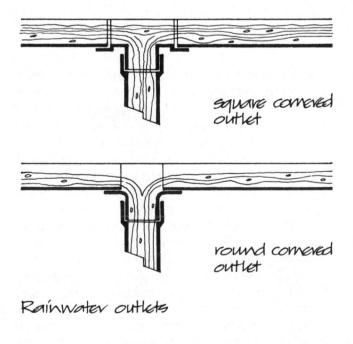

square cornered outlet

round cornered outlet

Rainwater outlets

Fig. 145

Calculation of gutter and rainwater pipe sizes: It is practice to use gutters and rainwater pipes large enough to collect, contain and discharge rainwater during short periods of intense rainfall that occur during storms. Rainfall intensities of 75 mm/hour occur for 5 minutes once in every four years and for 20 minutes once in every ten years and it is this intensity of rainfall that the gutter and rainwater pipes are designed to cope with.

The flow of rainwater from a roof to a gutter depends on the area of the roof draining to the gutter and whether the roof is flat or pitched and if pitched, on the angle of the pitch (slope).

A straightforward method of allowing for the slope of the roof and determining the effective area of a roof is set out in Table 12 in which the plan (horizontal) area of a pitched roof to be drained is multiplied by a factor relevant to the pitch of the roof. Having determined the effective area of the roof draining to a gutter, Table 13 is used to select a suitable size of gutter. The sizes shown in Table 13

Table 12. Calculation of area drained

Type of surface	Design area [m²]
1 flat roof	plan area of relevant portion
2 pitched roof at 30° pitched roof at 45° pitched roof at 60°	plan area of portion × 1.15 plan area of portion × 1.40 plan area of portion × 2.00
3 pitched roof over 70° or any wall	elevational area × 0.5

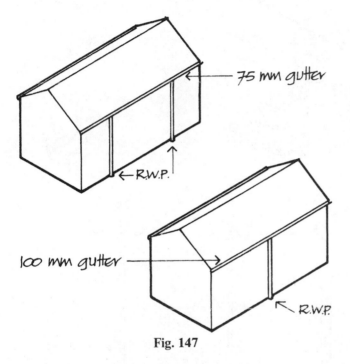

Fig. 147

Table 13. Gutter sizes and outlet sizes

Max roof area [m²]	Gutter size [mm dia]	Outlet size [mm dia]	Flow capacity [litres/sec]
6.0	—	—	—
18.0	75	50	0.38
37.0	100	63	0.78
53.0	115	63	1.11
65.0	125	75	1.37
103.0	150	89	2.16

Note
Refers to half round eaves gutters laid level with outlet at one end sharp edged. Round edged outlets allow smaller downpipe sizes.

are for half round gutters up to 8 metres long, laid level, and with one, sharp-edged outlet at only one end. Where the rainwater outlet is not at the end of a gutter and two lengths of gutter drain to one outlet, as illustrated in Fig. 147, then the larger of the areas draining into the outlet should be used to size the gutter and the outlets and rainwater down pipes may be up to 16 metres apart.

This method of determining the required size of gutter is perfectly satisfactory for most roofs and is appropriate to the sizes of gutter generally available.

The size of the rainwater down pipe required for different sizes of gutter is generally determined by the size of the outlet to that gutter size as set out in Table 13. A rainwater pipe should be at least the size of the gutter outlet. A down pipe that serves more than one gutter, by collecting the discharge from two outlets to a rainwater head, should have a cross sectional area at least as large as the combined areas of the outlets.

Eaves gutters and downpipes: Eaves gutters and downpipes for roofs are made of cast iron, pressed steel, aluminium, uPVC, sheet zinc or copper.

Cast iron is the traditional material. It is heavy, rigid, brittle and durable so long as it is protected by paint. Standard gutters are of half-round or ogee section with socket and spigot ends with angle, outlet and stop end fittings. The gutter joints are bedded in red lead putty or mastic and bolted together. Gutter lengths are supported by fascia or rafter brackets for half-round gutters and by screws or brackets for ogee gutters. Standard round-section socket and spigot downpipes with cast-on ears for fixing are used with offset and shoe fittings. The downpipes are secured to walls with pipe nails driven into hardwood plugs through distance pieces to fix the pipes away from the wall for painting. Fig. 146 is an illustration of cast-iron gutters and downpipes. Traditionally the large, oversized downpipes were fixed open jointed. Practice today is to make the joints of downpipes, fixed both externally and internally, with a mastic seal to contain the heavier flow resulting from the use of smaller pipes.

Galvanised and enamelled pressed steel gutters are round or ogee section with socket and spigot ends and fittings similar to those for cast iron. They are lighter in section and weight than cast iron. Galvanised gutters should be protected with paint while enamelled gutters are little used because of their high initial cost. Gutter fittings, pipes and fixings are similar to cast iron.

Cast aluminium gutters are segmental and ogee in section with socket and spigot ends and with fittings, fixings and downpipes similar to cast iron. They are lightweight, moderately rigid, brittle and require no protective coating. Since the advent of PVC rainwater goods this material is less used.

Standard uPVC gutters are made in half-round sections with sockets and spigot ends and angle, outlet and stop end fittings. Joints are made with a flexible seal and straps and the gutter fixed with fascia brackets. Round-section downpipes with socket and spigot ends for open joints or for a rubber seal ring are secured with metal brackets. Fig. 148 is an illustration of uPVC gutters and downpipes.

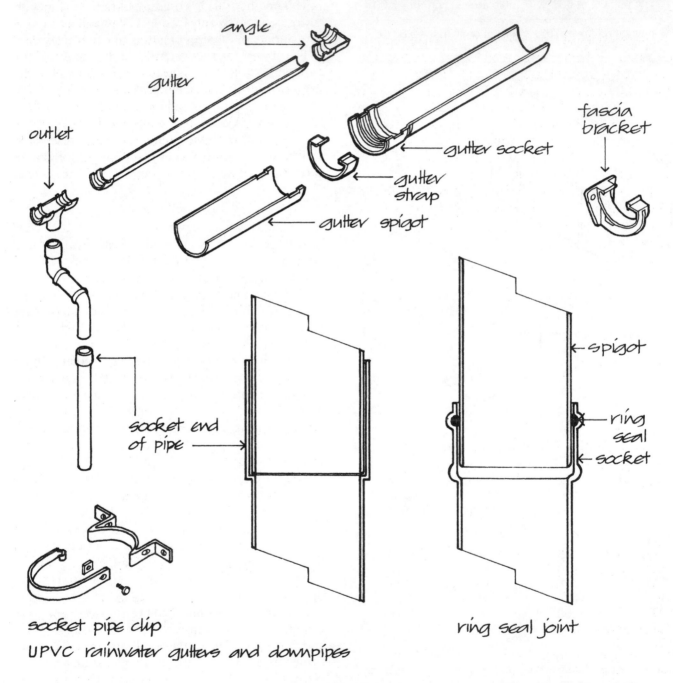

Fig. 148

uPVC is a lightweight material that needs no protective coating, is moderately rigid and has a smooth finish that encourages flow. It is the material most used for gutters and downpipes for domestic buildings today.

Sheet zinc and copper gutters and downpipes are little used. The flimsy section of the gutters and labour in fixing do not recommend the use of these materials.

Boundary wall and box gutters: The pitched roofs of industrial and other large span roofs drain to verge gutters of large section termed boundary wall or box gutters. Boundary wall gutters are so named because they are bedded on or fixed to the boundary wall to which the roof drains. Fig. 149 illustrates typical asbestos cement gutter sections. The gutters are fixed level and secured with straps or brackets and socket and spigot gutter ends are bedded in mastic and bolted. The application of these gutters to different roof coverings is illustrated in Vol. 3. The roof areas to drain to and rates of flow in these gutters are shown in Table 13.

Valley gutters collect and drain water from adjoining roofs. Valley gutters were in common use between short span timber roofs of larger buildings where slate, tile or lead-covered roofs drained to a common lead-lined timber-framed valley gutter. Since the advent of long span, light section roof trusses, valley gutters are used principally between adjacent pitched roofs over the large area industrial buildings illustrated in Vol. 3. Standard section asbestos cement or pressed steel gutters are used. Valley gutters have a level sole, sloping or vertical sides and a freeboard as illustrated in Fig. 150. The depth of a valley gutter should be such that rainwater run-off from both slopes will flow full at the head and half full at the outlet of the gutter. For unrestricted flow a valley gutter should discharge over a rainwater head. With long lengths of valley gutter intermediate outlets have to be provided and the flow into these is restricted by the size of the outlet.

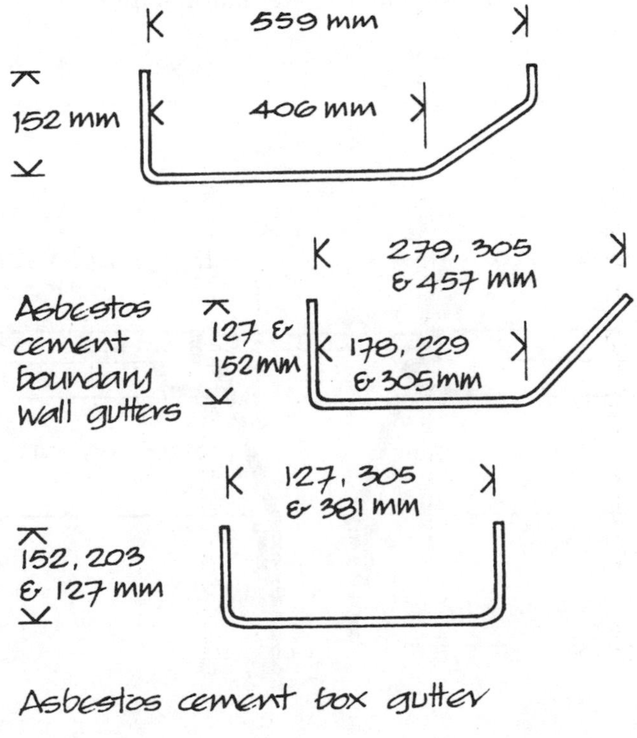

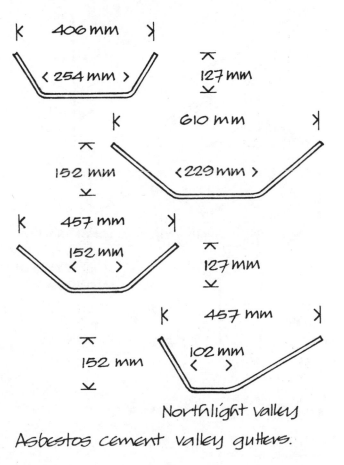

559 mm
152 mm
406 mm
279, 305 & 457 mm
Asbestos cement boundary wall gutters
127 & 152mm
178, 229 & 305mm
127, 305 & 381 mm
152, 203 & 127 mm
Asbestos cement box gutter

Fig. 149

406 mm
254 mm
127 mm
610 mm
152 mm
229 mm
457 mm
152 mm
127 mm
457 mm
152 mm
102 mm
Northlight valley
Asbestos cement valley gutters.

Fig. 150

FLAT ROOFS

Flat roofs are usually laid to a shallow fall towards
eaves gutters, outlets or channels and outlets, the fall
or slope of the roof being provided either by a
shallow slope in the roof itself or more usually by
timber firring or screeds laid to falls (see Vol. 1). The
drainage of rainwater from flat roofs is mainly
determined by the practical and economic need to
limit both the thickness of firring and screeds and the
number of outlets, and to economise in drain runs
underground.

There is, in theory, no limit to the size of a flat roof
that can be drained to one outlet providing the roof
covering is impermeable and there is a reasonable
upstand to contain water following storms. In
practice, however, considerations of economy in
screeds and outlets and the need to accommodate
expansion, limit flat roof areas.

Fig. 151 is an illustration of a lead chute draining
an asphalt-covered flat roof through an outlet in a
parapet to a rainwater head. The flat roof is laid to
falls towards the outlet. The width of the chute
depends on the area of roof that drains to the outlet
and the intensity of rainfall that the roof is designed
to cope with. It is reasonable to design flat roofs for
a rainfall intensity of 50 mm/h and a chute 300 mm
wide will drain 75 m² of roof at this rainfall intensity,
or up to 100 m² of roof with greater depth of flow,
that is a slower run-off.

Fig. 152 is an illustration of a bell-mouth outlet
draining a flat roof with a slope towards the centre of
the roof. The metal outlet and grating are set in the
roof and the roof finish is dressed around and over
the outlet which drains to a rainwater or downpipe
run inside the building. The area of roof that can
drain to these outlets is 75 m² for each 300 mm of the
perimeter of the outlet for rainfall intensities of 50
mm/h.

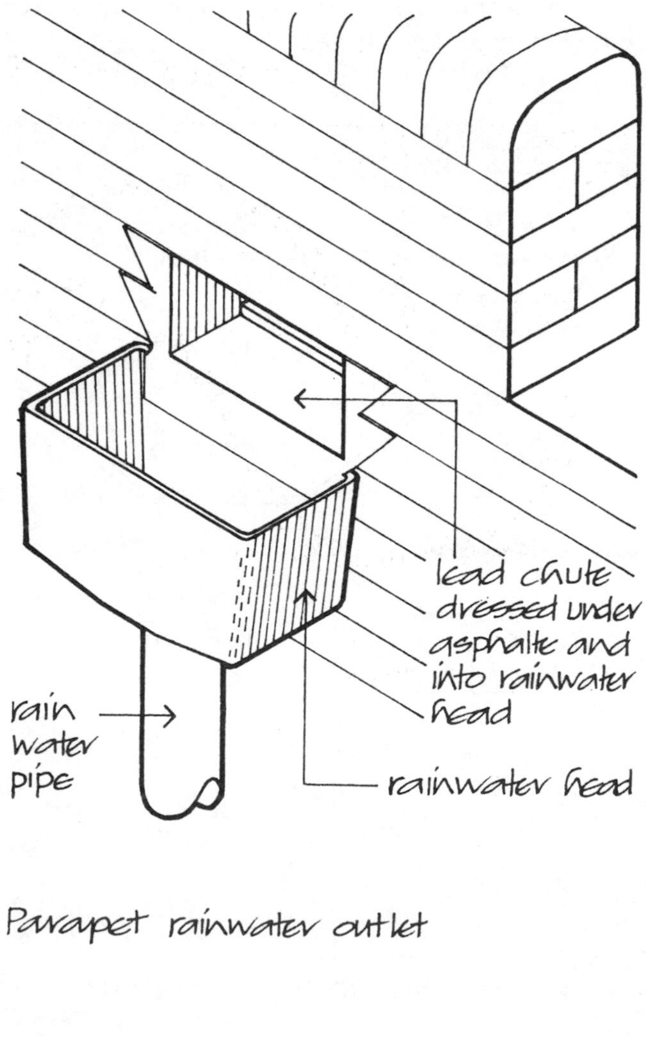

lead chute
dressed under
asphalte and
into rainwater
head

rain water pipe

rainwater head

Parapet rainwater outlet

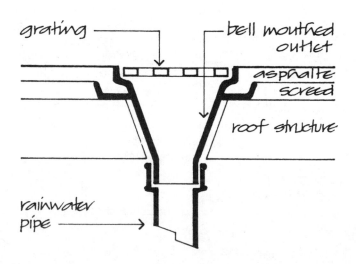

grating

bell mouthed outlet

asphalte
screed

roof structure

rainwater pipe

Fig. 151

Fig. 152

110

CONNECTION TO DRAINS

It was practice to discharge rainwater from down-pipes through a rainwater pipe shoe over a gulley. This is not considered good practice today because water splashing from the shoe is liable to make the adjacent wall damp. Practice today is to connect down pipes to a back inlet gully, trapped gullies being used where the drainage is a combined drain system and untrapped gullies where separate drain systems are used. Fig. 130 is an illustration of the connections of downpipes to gullies.

SURFACE-WATER DRAINAGE

Paved areas are laid to gradients or falls towards gullies or channels and gullies that collect surface water and discharge through drains to sewers or soakaways. The longitudinal gradient of access roads is 1 in 20 to 1 in 30, camber or crossfall 1 in 40 and the gradient of paved areas not less than 1 in 60. The paved area that drains to a gully depends on the gradient or fall, the type of surface being drained and the size of the gully used. Paved areas on level ground are usually laid in bays to fall towards a central gully. Where the ground slopes, paved areas usually fall towards a channel running down the slope to a gully or gullies as illustrated in Fig. 153. As a general guide a paved area of 200 to 250 m² at a gradient of 1 in 50 can be drained to one gully. The steeper the gradient the larger the area drained. At a gradient of 1 in 20 up to 500m² can drain to one gully.

The surface-water gullies are set in the paved areas as illustrated in Fig. 154. The graph in Fig. 155 shows the paved area that can be drained in relation to the size and gradient of pipe used.

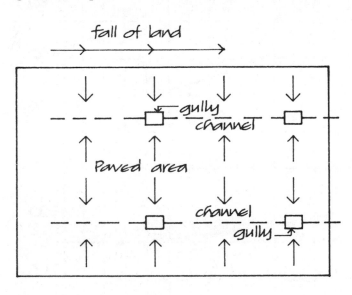

Fig. 153

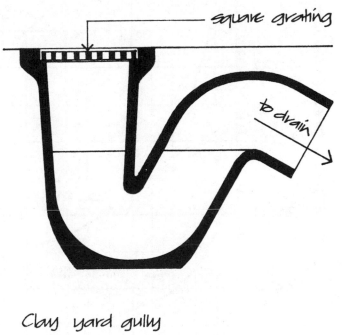

Clay yard gully

Fig. 154

111

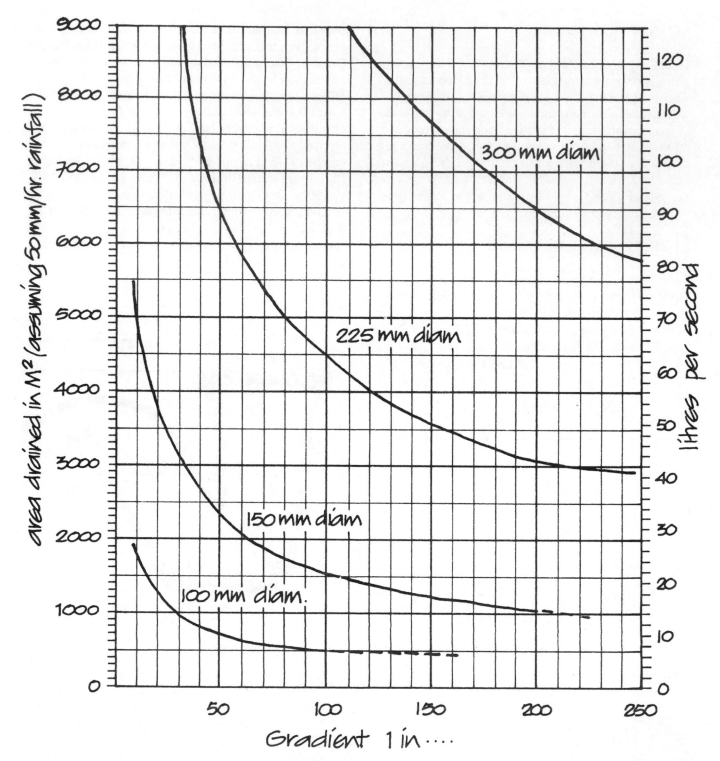

Graph for determining diameter & gradient
of surface water drains

Fig. 155

CHAPTER SIX

ELECTRICAL SUPPLY

SUPPLY AND DISTRIBUTION

Supply

In the United Kingdom the supply of electricity for buildings and for industry is generated in power stations by the Central Electricity Generating Board and distributed through the national grid which supplies electricity to fourteen area Electricity Boards. The national grid distributes electricity to all the Area Boards at 132,000 volts, mainly by over-head conductors. The high voltage distribution in the national grid is used to minimise loss in transmission. Supply from the national grid is converted by Area Boards to lower voltages of 11.000 or 6,600 volts, by transformers, to supply districts within the areas and then further reduced to 415 volts, by transformers, for local supply.

The electricity supply available to the majority of buildings is the standard low voltage supply of 415 volt, three-phase at 50 Hz frequency, through a cable consisting of three phase wires and a neutral wire, from the Area Board's local transformer sub-station.

Low voltage single or three phase supply: The voltage between any two of the three phase wires of the cable is 415 volts and the voltage between any one of the three phase wires and neutral wire is 240 volts. Where the anticipated demand on the supply of electricity, that is the load, is low, a 240 volt single phase supply connection from one phase wire and the neutral wire of the supply cable will be run into the building to provide a single phase supply. Where the anticipated load is high and also where the supply is for rotary equipment, which is invariably three phase, then a 415 volt three phase supply connection from two phase wires and the neutral wire of the supply cable will be run into the building.

High voltage supply: Where the anticipated loads on the electricity supply are high, as for example to heavy manufacturing industry and to a common supply to a large building or a number of buildings, it is necessary for the Area Board to provide a high voltage supply. The necessity for a high voltage intake is usually determined by the particular Area Board's policy on loading. The general division between low and high voltage intakes lies between 250 to 500 kVA.

The high voltage supply is connected to the Board's switch-gear from which a cable connects to the consumer's switchgear from which is run the consumer's supply to one or more transformers and switchgear, to one or more distribution centres in the building or on the site.

Tariffs and metering: The charge for the supply of electricity is measured by a meter installed by the Area Board and based on a tariff of units consumed. The tariffs, which vary between Area Boards, are in general:

    (1) An all-in tariff
    (2) Low voltage maximum demand tariff
and (3) High voltage maximum demand tariff

The all-in tariff is for small consumers, such as domestic premises, which consists of a quarterly standing charge plus a charge per unit consumed. In some areas a reduced charge for off-peak consumption during night time or week ends may be available.

Both the low voltage and high voltage maximum demand tariffs may be based on several component charges covering availability, actual maximum demand, units consumed and a fuel adjustment. These charges are usually variable and designed to encourage limitations of demand to match the supply available and off-peak demand use through lower unit charges.

The electricity supply authority has an obligation to provide a meter to record basic data, on which a tariff charge is applied. The majority of meters in use are of the induction type which record units consumed, to which a tariff is applied to calculate the charge to the consumer. The induction type of meter, which is liable to electrical and mechanical failure, should be serviced and must be withdrawn at intervals for testing, to comply with legal requirements.

Electronic meters are available and being installed in some areas. It is likely that electronic meters will gradually replace induction meters. The particular advantage of electronic meters is that remote reading of the meter is possible for computer recording at central points.

Fuses and circuit breakers: These are protective devices designed to operate under overload and short circuit conditions. Both fuses and circuit breakers are designed to cause a break in an electrical circuit to protect wiring from damage by over-heating caused by overload or short circuit. Fuses operate through the melting of a fuse wire and circuit breakers through a mechanical break in the circuit caused by a predetermined overload or short circuit. Because they operate by causing a break in a circuit, both fuses and circuit breakers are, in operation, circuit breakers.

Fuses: There are two basic types of fuse: (1) the semi-enclosed (rewirable) fuse and (2) the hbc (high breaking capacity) cartridge fuse.

The traditional semi-enclosed fuse consists of a

thin fuse wire, run between the terminals of a porcelain or bakelite holder, the terminals of which make contact when the holder is pushed into place in the fuse carrier. Fig. 156 is an illustration of a typical rewirable fuse holder. When the circuit suffers overload, the fuse wire melts and breaks the circuit. The disadvantages of the semi-enclosed fuse are that the fuse wire is too easily replaced with an incorrect size of wire, it has a higher fusing factor than hbc fuses, it deteriorates with time and is unreliable in conditions of short circuit. This traditional type of fuse will in time be superseded by hbc fuses or circuit breakers.

The hbc (high breaking capacity) cartridge fuse, in its simplest form, consists of a fuse wire in a tube with metal end caps to which the fuse wire is connected, as illustrated in Fig. 156, the fuse wire being surrounded by closely packed granular filler. The end caps serve as terminal for the fuse. When a circuit is overloaded, the fuse wire melts and breaks the circuit and the energy released is absorbed by the granular filler without damage to the fuse carrier.

These enclosed fuses do not deteriorate with time, nor damage the fuse holder. It is much simpler to change a cartridge type hbc fuse than rewire a semi-enclosed fuse. The smaller rated hbc cartridge fuses, such as the 3, 5 and 13 amp fuses, are extensively used in flat pinned plug tops for immediate protection of movable electrical equipment. The larger hbc fuses may be used as circuit breakers for all but the more heavily loaded circuits.

Miniature circuit breakers: A miniature circuit breaker is a moulded, sealed unit for use with single or three phase supplies. A circuit breaker is a magnetic-hydraulic or thermal-magnetic switching device designed to operate on overload to open the switch and break the connected circuit. A simple form of circuit breaker consists of a sealed tube filled with silicone fluid in which is a closely fitting iron slug. When overload occurs the magnetic pull of the coil surrounding the tube causes the iron slug to move through the tube and trip the circuit breaker switch, which closes. To test or make the circuit it is only necessary to open the switch which will remain open if the cause of the overload has been removed or will close if it has not. Miniature circuit breakers are more expensive than fuses but recommend themselves by the simplicity of operation. Fig. 157 is an illustration of a miniature circuit breaker.

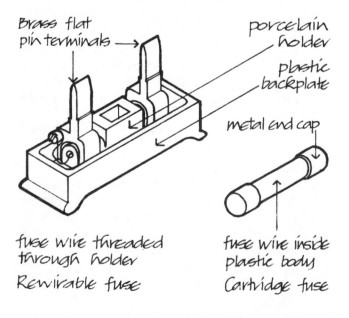

Brass flat pin terminals →
porcelain holder
plastic backplate
metal end cap

fuse wire threaded through holder
Rewirable fuse

fuse wire inside plastic body
Cartridge fuse

Fig. 156

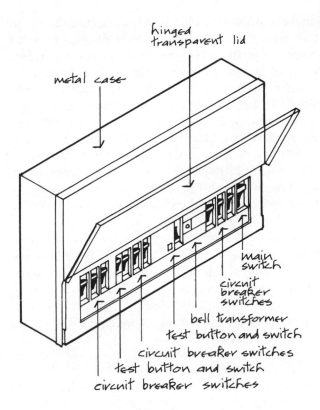

Minature circuit breaker consumer unit.

Fig. 157

Main distribution

Low voltage supplies: Where the anticipated load on the electricity supply is low, as for example to single domestic buildings, a low voltage supply is run into the building through a sealed box containing a main fuse, to a meter supplied by the Area Board, with meter tails for connection to the consumer's main switch and fuse unit.

Split main distribution: is necessary where, for example, there is a two part tariff and lighting is charged at a different rate than power. Here the supply cable is split to connect to two separate meters. Similarly a split main distribution is necessary where there are essential services, such as security systems, emergency lighting, computer installations and fire alarms, in addition to the basic non-essential supplies for lighting and power. The main distribution is split

between the non-essential and essential services with either batteries or a standby generator connected to the essential services through an automatic switch that operates when the supply is interrupted.

High voltage supplies: The high voltage supply necessary for large buildings, groups of buildings and manufacturing industry is run to the site by the supply authority to a transformer sub-station as necessary and connected to the authorities' main switch, circuit breaker equipment and meter. From the supply the consumer runs a main distribution cable system to each floor or group of floors to multi-storey blocks of flats or offices as illustrated in Fig. 158, or to transformer sub-stations at various load points on an extensive site.

For high voltage main distribution systems, armoured cables are generally used to feed trans-

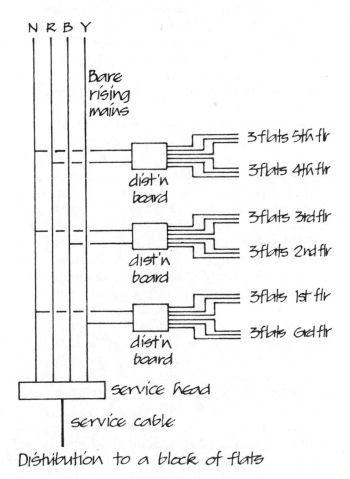

Distribution to a block of flats

Fig. 158

formers and switchgear at load points. Where heavy loads and frequent tap off points are required, as for example in multi-storey buildings, it is usual to use a busbar distribution system.

A busbar is a round or rectangular copper or aluminium bar conductor, prefabricated in a range of standard lengths. The busbars are either of bare copper which is supported at intervals by insulated carriers or the copper bars can be totally insulated. The advantage of the bare copper busbar is that sub or final circuits can readily be connected through tee-offs by clamping to rectangular section bars at any required point. The round section busbar requires shaped connectors for tees.

Busbars are run inside galvanised steel trunking in which there are insulating supports. Tap off boxes, complete with miniature circuit breakers, can be fixed to the trunking as necessary for sub or final circuits. For long lighting runs, for example, to supply fixed position lighting the busbar will generally be PVC insulated single-core cable supported inside metal trunking fixed to the underside of a floor or roof, with socket outlets for individual lights. For heavier loads on horizontal runs the insulated busbar will connect to terminals with plug in units, complete with circuit breakers, to connect to machine cable feeds.

Vertical risers of busbar distribution systems are usually run as bare rods supported by insulated carriers inside metal trunking from which fused tap-off points are connected to each floor for connection to final circuits. Vertical risers that are not inside a fire compartment must be provided with insulated barriers at each floor as fire stops.

Main distribution for high voltage supplies is run as either a radial or ring main system. Radial circuits run from the main switchboard to an outlet and back to the main switchboard, with a circuit breaker for each radial feeder. This is the simplest and cheapest form of circuit for high voltage main distribution, which is used for one or a few supply outlets. Ring main circuits run to a number of tap off points and back to the main switchboard with circuit breakers to each end of the ring system and switchgear for tapping off to radial feeders or transformers.

The advantage of a ring circuit is that it supplies a number of outlets, that additional outlets can be tapped off without shut downs and that maintenance on the feeder circuits is facilitated.

Final circuit distribution; Final circuits are those that feed directly to lighting or power fittings from the mains. In small buildings such as houses and shops, the final circuits run from one mains distribution board fixed close to the entry point of the mains supply. In larger buildings the final circuits run from single tap off points on radial or ring main circuits or from distribution boards connected to radial, ring or busbar mains distribution. The distinction between main and final circuits is in the anticipated loads which are heavier on the main than final circuits and affect the size of the necessary cable, switchgear and circuit breakers for the circuits.

For the sake of economy in the size of cable, switchgear and circuit breakers, final circuits are divided into various circuits depending on the anticipated loads and in larger installations into non-essential and essential services.

Final circuits for houses, shops and small offices are run separately for:

(1) Lighting from fixed ceiling and wall fittings
(2) Portable fittings such as air heaters, kitchen equipment and portable lamps
(3) Fixed equipment such as cookers and water heaters

For larger buildings final circuits are run separately for non-essential services such as:

(1) Lighting, fixed light fittings
(2) Small power fittings such as heaters and other portable equipment
(3) Lifts
(4) Air conditioning
(5) General plant and fixed equipment

and for essential services such as:

(1) Critical processes such as computers
(2) Security systems
(3) Emergency lighting
(4) Fire alarms
(5) Communications

Final Circuits: The two final electrical circuits used in buildings are the radial circuit and the ring circuit. In small buildings, such as houses, the single phase supply is connected, through a meter, to the consumer control unit which incorporates an isolating switch and fuse board or miniature circuit breakers from which up to twelve separate circuits may be run, one to each fuse or circuit breaker. Fig. 159 is an illustration of a consumer control unit.

When electricity was first used in domestic buildings in this country it was common to use three separate radial circuits, one rated at 2 A for lighting, one at 5A for small equipment and a third at 15 A for larger equipment. Each circuit was separately wired and fused for the purpose for which it was intended. With increases in the use of electrical appliances these variously fused radial circuits were liable to misuse and overload by the use of adaptors. The ring circuit was first used from the middle of this century to supply the increased number of socket outlets that were in demand in domestic buildings. The ring circuit runs from, and is protected by, the fuse in the distribution board to socket outlets and back to the fuseway. In the ring circuit system the cable of the circuit is protected by the fuse in the distribution board and the flexible cord and its appliance by a cartridge fuse in the plug. Plugs are fitted with either 3, 5, or 13 A fuses to suit the flexible cord and appliance to which they are connected. In this way the fuse protecting the circuit is separate from that protecting the individual appliances and their flexible cables. Providing the correct fuse is fitted to the plug, then an appliance can be connected to any socket outlet on a ring circuit and a standard socket and plug be used. Fig. 160 is a diagrammatic illustration of a ring circuit. An advantage of the ring circuit is that the current can circuit to the outlet around both halves of the ring so that the circuit cable carries at most, half of the total current in the whole circuit. Thus the fuse rating can be greater than the cable rating.

Where it would be extravagant to run the ring circuit to one or two isolated outlets and then back, it is practice to employ a spur which is a radial circuit spur off the ring circuit. The cable to these spurs outlets will carry the full load of the supply and it must be protected by a separate fuse by the use of a fused spur box as illustrated in Fig. 160. The particular use of spurs from ring circuits is to fixed appliances such as fixed electric fires, the fused spur box serving the same purpose as the fuse in a plug in protecting the individual appliance.

The ring circuit or radial circuit to socket outlets is called a power circuit because the cable and fuses of the circuit are designed for loads common to power

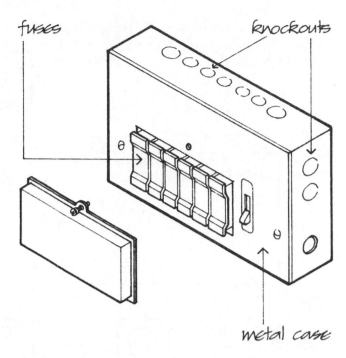

Consumer Control Unit

Fig. 159

supply even though lighting may be connected to it.

A separate lighting circuit is used for fixed ceiling and wall lights and these radial circuits are run separately from the distribution board or consumer control unit. The cable to domestic lighting circuits is generally run and fused at 5 A and up to eight 150 W lights may be connected to each circuit. The rating of a domestic lighting circuit is limited by the flexible cord used in ceiling pendants which is usually 0.75 mm^2 and rated at 6A. In extensive installations, where fixed lights without flexible cords are used, the circuit may be run in cable fused at 15 A to serve many lighting outlets and so reduce the number of circuits.

To connect several lighting outlets on a radial circuit it is usual to 'loop in'. This system of looping in, illustrated in Fig. 160 for a ring circuit, describes the method of making joints in cable at outlets rather than at connectors or junction boxes. Joints at outlets are of easy access for maintenance or repair. Fig. 161 shows the looping in system applied to a lighting circuit. It will be seen that one length of cable runs to a lighting outlet, another to the next with other lengths of cable to the switches. In this way separate lengths of cable are joined at outlets and there is no need for a joint in cable lengths.

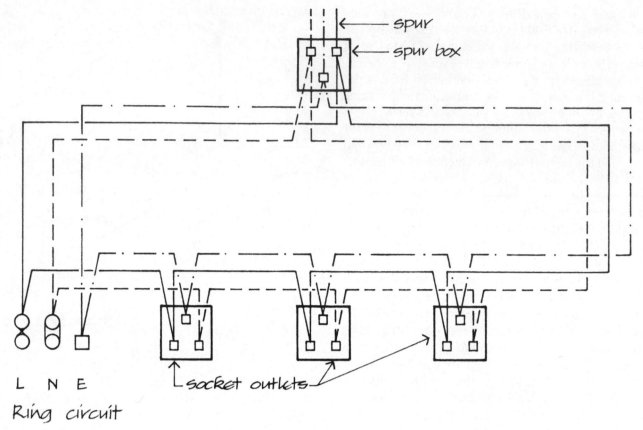

L   N   E

Ring circuit

socket outlets

spur

spur box

Fig. 160

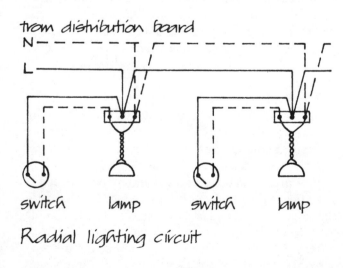

from distribution board

N

L

switch   lamp   switch   lamp

Radial lighting circuit

Fig. 161

Cable and conduit: Electricity is conducted along wires of copper which have to be insulated and also protected against mechanical damage. Insulated wire or wires are commonly termed cable to distinguish them from bare wire. Small cables for connecting movable fittings such as lamps are termed flex, or flexible wire or cable. The wire in cable is often stranded, each wire being made from a number of small wires twisted to form one conductor. A cable made of small twisted wires is easier to manipulate than a cable with single wires. Small metric size cable is made either of single or stranded wires. The size of the cable is described by the cross-sectional area of the wire as for example 1.5mm^2.

The majority of cables used for electrical wiring in building today are insulated and sheathed in PVC which is a tough, incombustible, chemically inert plastic that does not deteriorate with age. PVC softens at temperatures above 80°C and should not be used where ambient temperatures are above 70°C.

Many cables insulated with PVC have a thicker PVC sheath over the PVC insulation to the individual wires and this cable is described as PVC Insulation PVC Sheathed Cable, abbreviated PVC-PVC. Several insulated wires can be contained in the same sheath with a bare earth wire. Fig. 162 is an illustration of twin and earth PVC/PVC the sheath enclosing twin insulated wires and a bare earth wire. PVC cable without conduit is run in hollow floors of timber and steel and inside pitched roofs to socket and lighting outlets.

Vulcanised india rubber cable was extensively used before PVC cable was first produced. The cable consists of an inner layer of rubber around tinned copper wires with an outer coating of vulcanised rubber. The rubber coating of this cable becomes brittle with age and fails, needing rewiring after some twenty years. It is little used in building today.

Mineral Insulated Metal Sheathed cable (M.I.M.S.) consists of single-stranded wires tightly compressed in magnesium oxide enclosed in a seamless metal sheath of copper or aluminium as illustrated in Fig. 162. The combination of the excellent insulation of the magnesium oxide and the metal sheath gives this cable an indefinite life and good resistance to mechanical damage. It is used in building where its high initial cost is justified, for example in building into floors and walls.

The insulation and sheath to cable such as PVC provides some protection against damage during building operations. In many situations the sheath does not provide sufficient protection and it is usual to run cable inside metal or plastic conduit which provides protection and facilitates withdrawing and renewing cable if necessary.

Metal conduit consists of steel tubes, couplings and bends which are either coated with black enamel or galvanised, the latter coating specifically for use where conduit is exposed. Fig. 163 is an illustration of typical steel conduit. The nominal bore of steel conduit is its outside diameter, for example 20 mm. Light- and heavy-gauge conduit is manufactured, light gauge with screwed push-fit joints, and heavy with screwed connections. Heavy-gauge conduit is of sufficient section to act as the earth conductor for cable without an earthwire and all connections should make good electrical contact.

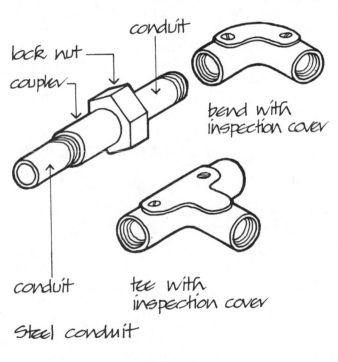

Fig. 163

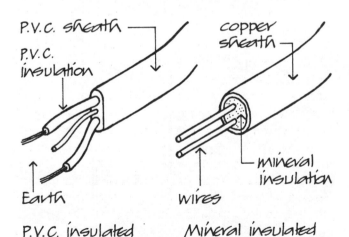

Fig. 162

PVC conduit has been much used in recent years in place of steel conduit as it is cheaper and more easily installed. It is made in round and oval sections the latter for burying in plaster. The conduit is joined with couplers that are solvent cemented to the conduit. Fig. 164 is an illustration of typical PVC conduit. High impact grade PVC conduit is used for its resistance to mechanical damage. PVC is not a conductor so that cable with an earth wire is used with it.

Cable is run in conduit in the structure of buildings where it is buried in floors, walls and finishes such as plaster and screeds.

Where several cables are run together it is usual to protect them inside metal or plastic trunking. Metal trunking is made from 18-gauge sheet steel in square or rectangular sections one side of which is a screwed or clip on lid for access. Various elbows and gusset tees are made for angles. Trunking is generally too bulky to bury in the structure of buildings and has to be accommodated in ducts and false ceilings. Fig. 165 is an illustration of typical trunking.

Earthing: Fuses and M.C.B.s in distribution boards and fuses in ring circuit plugs are designed to break a circuit at predetermined current rating to protect the circuit cable, flex and appliance from damage by overheating.

As protection against damage to property by fire and protection against a serious electric shock to persons, that may be caused by a failure of the insulation to electrical installations, it is practice to 'earth' the installation. The term 'earthing' describes the method of providing a path of low resistance to currents that might flow to earth due to a failure of insulation.

Both the mains supply cable to the building and the electrical installation in the building are 'earthed'. The mains supply cable is earthed by connecting its metal sheath to earth either by connection to an incoming metal service pipe or to a plate or rod buried in the ground.

The internal installation is earthed by the connection of a separate earth wire, the protective conductor, or metal trunking, or metal conduit to earth through a conductor wire, connected to metal service pipes such as gas and water pipes that run uninterrupted into the ground.

Where there is no satisfactory low resistance conductor such as metal pipes, then the earth wire, metal trunking or metal conduit has to be connected directly to an earthing plate or rod securely buried in the ground.

Switches and outlets: A switch makes or interrupts a circuit and is used by itself for lighting circuits or as part of an outlet. A switch consists of the rocker-operated switch mechanism and its front plate and a box to contain the switch. Switch and outlet boxes are of metal of sizes suited to the switch or outlet to be housed and depths suited to recessed or surface fixing. Fig. 166 is an illustration of typical boxes for

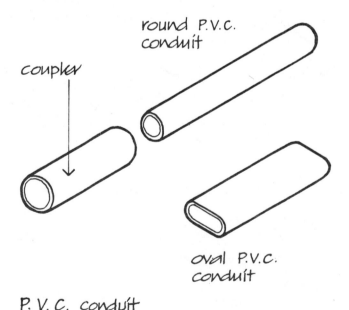

round P.V.C. conduit

coupler

oval P.V.C. conduit

P. V. C. conduit

Fig. 164

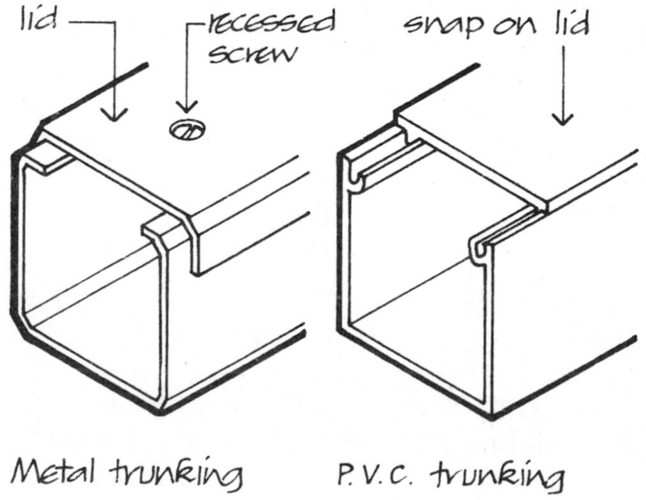

lid — recessed screw

snap on lid

Metal trunking   P.V.C. trunking

Fig. 165

switches and outlets. The boxes are fitted to a recess or a chase in walls, fixed to walls for recessing in plaster or fixed on the surface. The plastic front plate and switch or switches illustrated in Fig. 166 are screwed to the metal box.

Socket outlets, popularly known as power points, consist of a box, socket outlet and front plate. The socket outlet is designed to accept a plug connected to the flexible wire of an appliance as illustrated in Fig. 167. The metal box which houses the outlet and to which the front plate is screwed is for recessing into walls, plaster, or for surface fixing. The majority

of socket outlets are of the 13 A type on a ring circuit, the plug holding cartridge fuses of 3, 5, 10 and 13 A rating to suit the flex and appliance they serve. The plugs to 13 A outlets have square pins as illustrated in Fig. 167. Outlets for lighting fittings for radial circuits to wall switches are rated at 2 A to accept round-pin plugs as illustrated in Fig. 167.

It is likely that a standard 16 A outlet will, before long, become standard in this country to conform to European standards for use with round three-pin plugs.

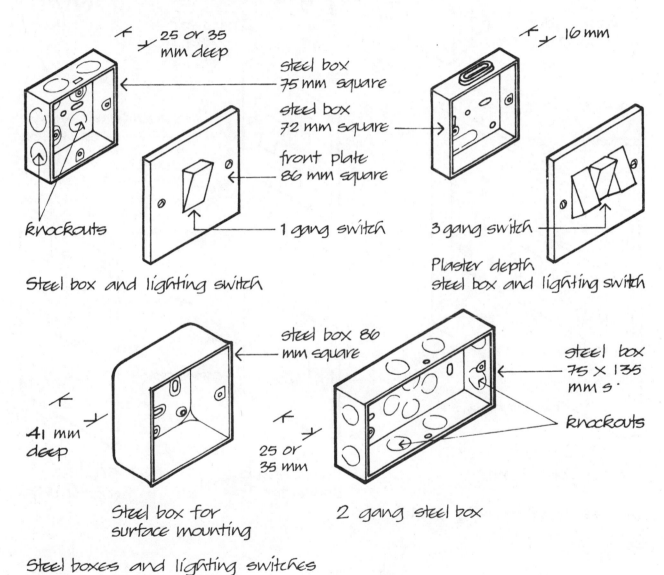

Fig. 166

121

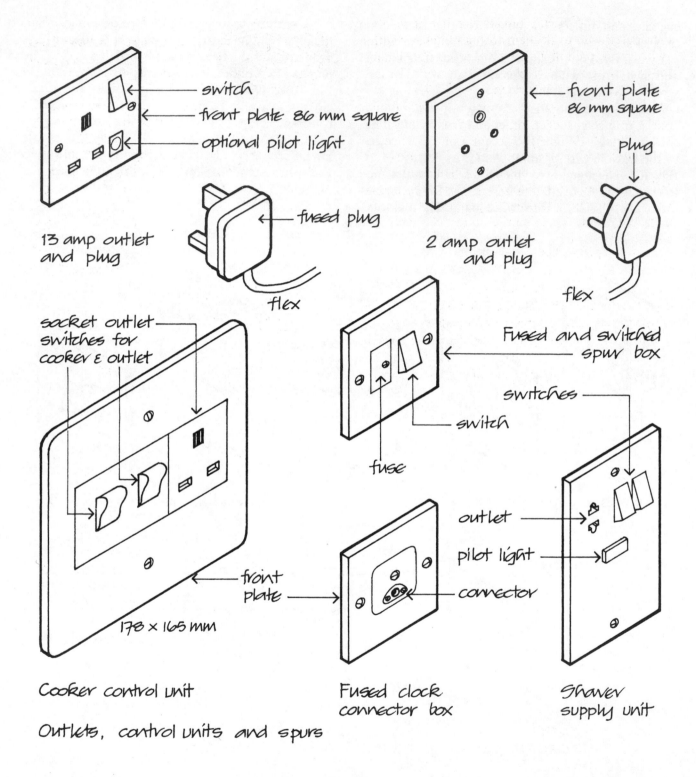

switch

front plate 86 mm square

optional pilot light

13 amp outlet and plug

fused plug

flex

front plate 86 mm square

plug

2 amp outlet and plug

flex

socket outlet switches for cooker & outlet

Fused and switched spur box

switch

fuse

switches

outlet

pilot light

connector

front plate

178 × 165 mm

Cooker control unit

Fused clock connector box

Shaver supply unit

Outlets, control units and spurs

Fig. 167

122

Because ring circuit outlets are live it is often considered wise to fit them with a switch, or with a switch and pilot light to give protection against misuse and possible danger. Outlets with switches and pilot lights are illustrated in Fig. 167.

Where a radial spur is run from a ring circuit a fused spur box, illustrated in Fig. 167, is used and housed in a metal box.

Electric cookers are supplied by a separate radial circuit run to a cooker control box illustrated in Fig. 167. The supply to the cooker is run from the box which is generally fitted with a plug outlet for small electrical kitchen appliances. Outlets designed for specific electrical equipment such as clocks and shavers are illustrated in Fig. 167.

Lampholders and roses: Domestic ceiling lights may be of the flexible pendant type, illustrated in Fig. 168, consisting of the ceiling rose, pendant flex and lampholder. The ceiling rose covers a plastic housing and terminal block screwed to the ceiling and the lampholders, illustrated in Fig. 168, may be fixed to walls or ceilings.

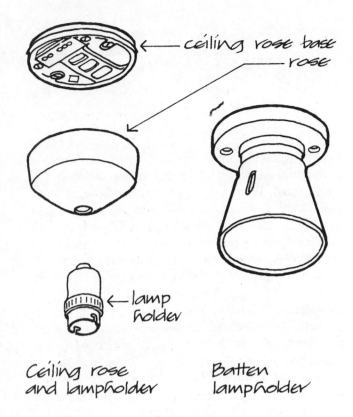

ceiling rose base
rose

lamp holder

Ceiling rose and lampholder

Batten lampholder

Fig. 168

CHAPTER SEVEN

GAS SUPPLY

Town Gas, first produced in 1812, is the combination of combustible gases from the carbonisation (heating) of coal. Each town had its own gasworks and gasholders supplying gas for lighting, cooking and heating, hence the name town gas. A by-product of the heating or carbonisation of coal to produce town gas was coke which was extensively used as a cheap fuel for heating. With the introduction of electricity the demand for gas declined. During the first half of the twentieth century there was keen competition between the suppliers of gas and electricity to the advantage of the consumer. The advantage of a lighting and heating source at a competitive rate at the touch of a switch led to the change-over from gas to electricity first for lighting and later for domestic heating. The manufacture of town gas required a large site, a ready source of high quality coal and a considerable labour force all of which were becoming increasingly scarce and expensive.

Natural gas, first imported from North Africa in 1964 and supplied to consumers has, since 1968, come from the North Sea fields which, it is estimated, have known reserves sufficient for current and future consumption well into the twenty-first century. Natural gas is mainly methane, has twice the calorific value of town gas and is a high grade controllable fuel eminently suited to both domestic and commercial uses for heating. Since the introduction of natural gas its use by industry and commerce has increased fourfold. Unlike town gas, natural gas is non-toxic and as it is odourless, additives give warning of leaks by their distinctive smell. Natural gas is delivered to the consumer at pressures two to three times greater than town gas and in consequence pipes about half the bore of those needed for town gas can be used.

Small gas burning appliances such as single point water heaters and cookers do not need a flue as the products of combustion may safely disperse to a ventilated room. Larger gas appliances such as multipoint water heaters, gas fires and boilers require a flue to carry the non-polluting products of combusion to the open air. A typical built-in gas flue is illustrated in Vol. 2.

Since 1968 most existing town gas burning appliances have been converted to use natural gas and all new appliances are designed to burn natural gas. The conversion of existing town gas burning appliances to burn natural gas was effectively completed in 1976.

Service pipe: Gas is supplied under pressure through the gas main from which a branch service pipe is run underground to buildings. The service pipe is laid to fall towards the main so that condensate runs back to the main where it is collected in buckets. Where the consumption of gas is high, as in commercial and other large buildings, a valve is fitted to the service pipe just inside the boundary of the site to give the Supplier control of the supply, for example in the case of fire. Domestic service pipes are run directly into the building without a valve at the boundary and the meter valve or cock controls the supply.

The gas service pipe must not enter a building under the foundation of a wall or loadbearing partition to avoid the possibility of damage to the pipe by settlement of the foundations. Gas service pipes run through walls and solid floors must pass through a sleeve, as illustrated in Fig. 169, so that settlement or movement does not damage the pipe. The sleeve is usually cut from a length of steel or plastic pipe larger than the service pipe which is bedded in mastic to make a watertight joint.

A meter installation comprises a cock, governor, filter and a meter, for domestic premises, with the addition of a thermal cut-out and non-return valve for larger installations. Most domestic meters are inside the building for the convenience of the occupier. Meter installations to large premises are often in a purpose built meter house. Where possible, domestic meters installations are outside the premises in a position affording shelter such as in a basement area under steps, or in a box, or housing giving shelter. The advantage of fitting the meter outside is that it is naturally ventilated and in a position where the meter reader can gain access when the occupier is out.

Gas cock (valve): A gas cock to control the supply from the service pipe to the governor and meter consists of a solid plug that in the shut position fills the bore of the cock and in the open position only partly obstructs the flow of gas. The gas cock is operated by a hand lever as illustrated in Fig. 170. The connection of the gas cock to the pressure governor is made with a short length of semi-rigid stainless steel tube which can accommodate any movement between the service pipe and meter which might otherwise damage the meter. The semi-rigid tube is illustrated in Fig. 170.

Pressure governor and filter: A combined pressure governor and filter is fitted at the connection of the service pipe to the meter as illustrated in Fig. 170, for domestic installations, and a separate governor and

filter for larger installations. The fine mesh filter is fitted to collect pulverised particles of rust and metal which are carried along the main by gas. But for the filter these fine particles would clog gas jets to gas burning appliances. The governor is a spring loaded diaphragm valve the function of which is to reduce the pressure of gas in the main to a pressure suited to gas burning appliances. The governor reduces mains gas pressure to that equivalent to 8 inch (203 mm) water gauge.

Gas meter: The meter illustrated in Fig. 170 is the traditional tincase gas meter. The light gauge tincase contains bellows that fill with gas through a valve and then discharge gas to the distribution pipe so that the movement of filling and emptying operates the meter that records the volume of gas supplied. As the meter records the volume of gas supplied it should not be near to a heat source else the consumer will be paying for the heated and therefore greater volume of gas to his disadvantage. Because of the flimsy construction of the tin-case meter it is practice to

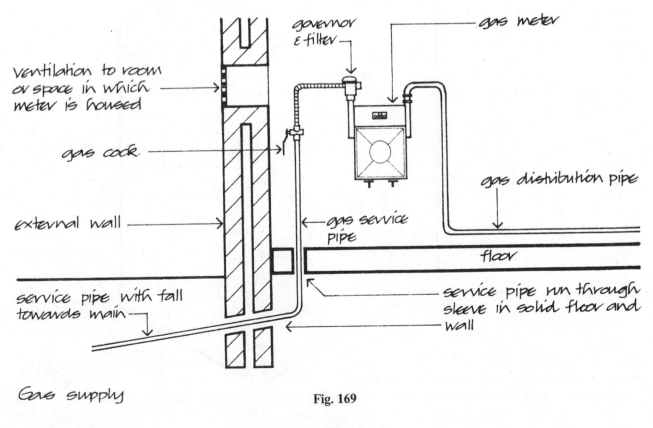

Gas supply

Fig. 169

125

make connections of service and distribution pipes with either a semi-rigid stainless steel tube or a short length of lead pipe which can take up any movement and so prevent damage to the meter. A semi-rigid and a lead pipe connection are illustrated in Fig. 170.

Steelcase gas meters are available which comprise a rigid steel case and compact bellows so that a steelcase meter is appreciably smaller than a tincase meter of the same capacity. Steelcase meters are from two thirds to half the size of a tincase meter of similar capacity. Because of the greater rigidity of the steelcase it is practice to make the service pipe connection with a semi-rigid tube and the distribution pipe with a rigid connection. Where gas consumption is large a rotary displacement meter is used.

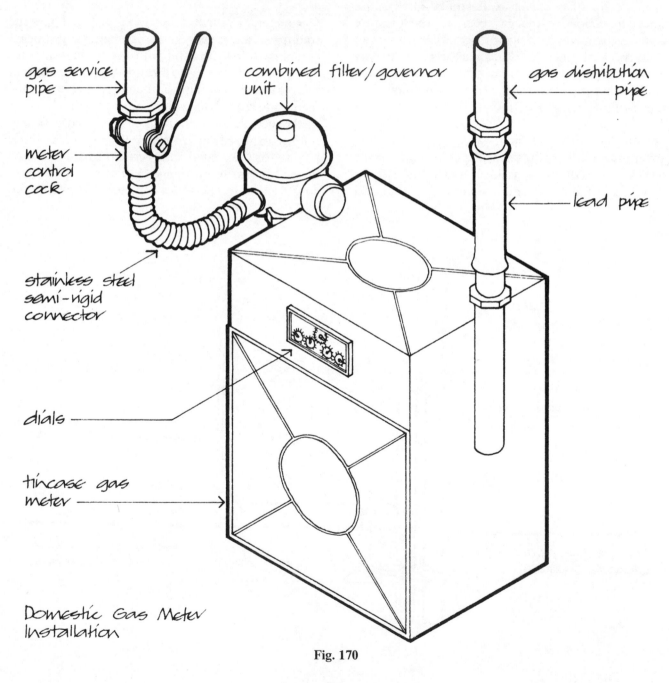

gas service pipe

combined filter/governor unit

gas distribution pipe

meter control cock

lead pipe

stainless steel semi-rigid connector

dials

tincase gas meter

Domestic Gas Meter Installation

Fig. 170

126

Where interruption of the gas supply for maintenance, repair or replacement of the meter or governor is unacceptable, as in hospitals and some industries, it is usual to install a meter bypass. A bypass is a length of pipe connected directly between the service pipe and the distribution pipe to bypass the meter. There should be a separate gas cock, governor and filter in the bypass so that the meter cock may be closed for maintenance or repair work and the bypass cock opened meantime to continue the supply.

The room or space in which a gas meter is installed should be permanently ventilated to the open air against escape of gas and build up of heat. A small air brick or vent suffices for most domestic installations and ventilation equivalent to 4% of the floor area for larger installations.

Gas pipes: The majority of both gas service and distribution pipes are run in mild steel tubulars, the pipes having the natural steel finish as galvanising coatings are affected by gas. Gas tubulars have screwed connections the same as those used for water pipes. Mild steel gas tubulars run underground and in plaster should be protected with a bituminous wrapping or coating.

CHAPTER EIGHT

REFUSE STORAGE

The volume of loosely packed refuse from an average three person household is 0.09m³ per week, slightly less than the capacity of a standard 0.092 m³ dustbin. The larger part of the volume of domestic refuse today is bulky lightweight paper and plastic wrapping and container material which in our 'throw away' style of living is increasing to the extent that it is estimated that the volume of refuse from an average three person household will increase to 0.12m² before long. This bulky refuse encourages the householder to compress as much as possible into his refuse bin which makes it difficult to discharge the contents into the refuse collection vehicle. The bin is damaged by banging it against the vehicle to empty it and in a short time it too becomes refuse and the cycle of waste accelerates. The smaller part of domestic refuse is ash from solid fuel appliances, tins, bottles and kitchen waste. The last, if not wrapped, may adhere to the side of the bin, putrefy and be the source of disagreeable odours and be a breeding ground for flies.

The usual sequence in the storage of domesstic refuse is the filling of a binette or other small receptacle inside the dwelling, which is emptied into a refuse bin, a larger refuse storage container or into a refuse chute discharging to a refuse container. Collection is usually once or twice a week. Bins are collected from the premises or from the kerbside depending on access and local arrangements and the larger containers are usually collected from the premises by vehicles designed for the purpose. The required capacity of refuse containers depends, therefore, on an assumption of about 0.3m³ refuse per person and the frequency of collection. It is sensible to provide a larger capacity than this average, per person, against interruption of collection during holiday periods and festivals when the volume of bulky lightweight refuse increases considerably, otherwise bins will be packed and difficult to empty and also to provide adequate capacity against spillage of refuse. An additional capacity of from ten to twenty-five percent over average is not unusual.

Dustbins (refuse bins): Refuse bins are still generally described as dustbins from the days when the solid fuel fire was the principal source of heat and the resultant volume of dust and ash that was discharged to bins gave them their name. At that time a more frugal style of living did not produce the volume of refuse common today.

Galvanised mild steel dustbin: This is the traditional dust or refuse bin that has only recently been superseded by the plastic bin and the paper sack. A soundly made galvanised steel dustbin is robust and will give useful service for many years providing the zinc coating (galvanising) is not damaged by mishandling. Once the zinc coating wears the mild steel rapidly rusts and the bin disintegrates. The British Standard mild steel dustbin illustrated in Fig. 171, is round in section and tapers from top to bottom to facilitate emptying and also stacking. There is a reinforcing turnover rim, slightly dished bottom, lifting handles and a loose lid as illustrated in Fig. 171. Standard bins are 0.028(1), 0.056(2), 0.071(2½), and 0.092(3¼) cubic meters capacity, the figures in brackets being the equivalent (ft³) capacities. The 0.071 and 0.092 m³ bins are those most used. A standard steel bin is heavy, about 12 kg, and when full it is near the limit in weight that can be lifted and emptied by an average person without strain.

Various non-standard light section galvanised steel bins are manufactured, mostly from corrugated or fluted sheet to reinforce the flimsy material. Because of the light section material from which they are made they have an appreciably shorter life than the heavier standard bin and refuse that collects in the troughs of the corrugated or fluted sides is difficult to clean. These bins, though somewhat cheaper, are a false economy.

Rubber lids and rubber bases to steel bins are available to reduce the noise of handling the bins.

A specialised-steel bin, the dustless loading bin, is manufactured for the storage and emptying of ash and other dusty refuse. The lid is hinged to the bin

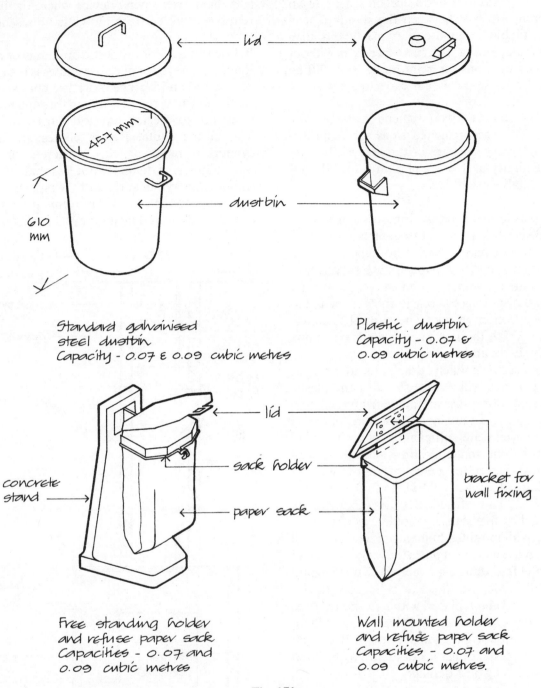

Standard galvanised
steel dustbin
Capacity - 0.07 & 0.09 cubic metres

Plastic dustbin
Capacity - 0.07 &
0.09 cubic metres

Free standing holder
and refuse paper sack
Capacities - 0.07 and
0.09 cubic metres

Wall mounted holder
and refuse paper sack
Capacities - 0.07 and
0.09 cubic metres.

Fig. 171

and so designed that it does not open until the bin has been lifted by the special collection vehicle and sealed against a shutter for dustless emptying. This type of bin is too heavy for manhandling and has to be wheeled on a trolley to the collection vehicle.

Plastic refuse bins are about half the weight of a standard steel bin of the same capacity and if made of high density polyethylene or polypropylene are rigid, durable, easy to clean and may have a useful life of several years if reasonably handled, and they do not deteriorate by oxidisation as do steel bins. There is no great difference in cost between the standard steel and the plastic bin. A good quality plastic bin, such as that illustrated in Fig. 171, has taper sides without flutes or corrugations, a reinforcing rim, lifting handles and a loose lid. Usual capacities are 0.071 and 0.092 m³.

Lightweight, low density polythene plastic bins are manufactured with corrugated sides for reinforcement. These flimsy bins are brittle and easily fractured, particularly at low temperatures and do not have a reasonable useful life.

Paper and plastic refuse sacks: First used in Scandinavia the disposable paper refuse sack is an alternative to the steel or plastic bin for householders. The obvious advantage of the paper refuse sack is that both the soiled container and its contents are collected and disposed of in one journey from and to the refuse collection vehicle. The natural resource, wood, from which the sacks are made is becoming increasingly scarce and expensive in our throw away society and it seems unlikely, despite its advantages, that the paper sack will replace the steel and plastic bin. Paper sacks for refuse are made from stout two ply wet strength paper or single ply waterproof kraft paper. These sacks are sufficiently robust to stand outside between normal collections and to store all but the most jagged of items of refuse without damage. Bags of capacity 0.071 and 0.092 m³ are generally used. The refuse sacks are supported by wall mounted or free standing holders as illustrated in Fig. 171. Wall mounted holders are fixed to a wall with a back plate which supports the sack holder and its lid and the free standing concrete or metal stand support sack holder and lid. For collection the full sack is unclipped and replaced with a fresh one. Free standing holders are heavy enough to stand in high wind and remain upright against knocks. Both wall mounted and freestanding sack holders may be fitted with wire guards against damage.

Plastic sacks have been used instead of paper sacks, the plastic sacks being cheaper than paper, require less space for storage of sacks and do not deteriorate in damp conditions. Plastic sacks are fixed to wall mounted or free standing holders similar to those illustrated for paper sacks.

To date the majority of paper and plastic refuse sacks have been supplied by local refuse collection authorities as a part of their refuse collection service

as a manpower saving device where the bulk of the refuse is collected from individual households.

Refuse Chute: For domestic buildings of more than four floors a system of refuse chutes is the best means of disposal and storage. A refuse chute is a vertical shaft into which refuse is tipped through hoppers, the refuse being collected and stored in a container at the foot of the chute. Refuse chutes are lined with cylindrical pipes of clay, concrete or asbestoscement, internal diameter not less than 450 mm, the smooth impervious surface of the pipes providing the least impediment to the movement of the refuse down the chute and facilitating cleansing by periodic

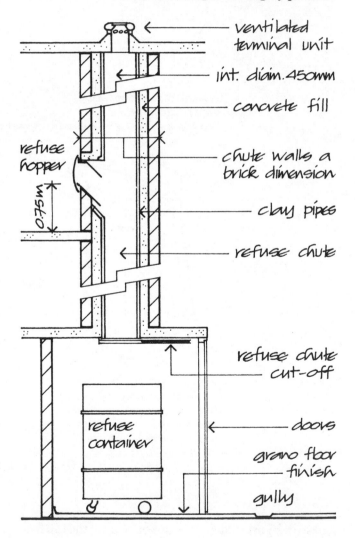

Refuse chute and container chamber

Fig. 172

hosing down. The lining pipes are enclosed in a brick or concrete shaft for their support and as a protection against spread of fire. Metal hoppers at each floor level provide entry points to the chute. The opening to these hoppers should not exceed 350 mm in width and 250 in height. Hoppers to chutes should be located on open communal access balconies or well ventilated lobbies away from habitable rooms or in separate well ventilated lobbies of fire resisting construction off main circulation lobbies. At the foot of each chute there should be a container chamber as illustrated in Fig. 172. When the refuse container is full, the chute is closed by the steel shutter and the full container replaced with an empty one, and the shutter opened. Depending on the anticipated volume of refuse a variety of arrangements for containers is available such as the single 0.95 m³ wheeled container illustrated in Fig. 172, a range of single containers on a turntable, a range of refuse sacks on a turntable or a single large container.

Refuse chutes should be carried up to or above roof level with a ventilating terminal of the same diameter as the chute or where this is not possible with a reduced ventilating pipe and terminal. Ventilation of the chute and the lobbies in which the hoppers are located is essential.

With sensible use, reasonable periodic changes of container to avoid spillage and cleansing of the chute and container chamber, the refuse chute is a satisfactory system of storage for refuse in multi-storey buildings.

Refuse containers are large metal containers in which refuse, both domestic and trade, is stored. The limit to the size of these containers is the capacity of a collection vehicle to lift and carry or tow away the container. The galvanised steel container illustrated in Fig. 173, is often described as a Paladin container. These containers are wheeled for manhandling to the collection vehicle which is designed to lift, upturn and empty the contents into the rear of the vehicle. To this end there are various lifting attachments to the container such as the studs shown in Fig. 173, or angle iron rims to suit the various makes of collection vehicle. These standard 0.95 m³ refuse containers are extensively used at the foot of chutes for communal and trade refuse. A wide variety of large, purpose constructed, galvanised steel containers are available principally for storage at the foot of chutes and for trade waste.

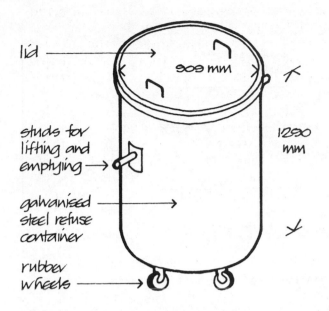

Galvanised mild steel refuse storage container - Capacity - 0.95 cubic metres

Fig. 173

The Garchey system is a method of waste disposal in which refuse is fed through an enlarged waste outlet in the sink into a waste tube housed inside a refuse receiver fitted below the sink. Waste water from the sink runs into and fills the waste receiver illustrated in Fig. 174. When the waste tube is filled it is raised by the householder and its contents are washed down the waste to the 150 mm waste stack to the collection chamber. All waste water appliances are connected to the waste stack so that their discharges assist in washing down the refuse. Soil appliances are drained to a separate stack. The Garchey refuse collection chamber is emptied once a week to a tanker which de-waters and compacts the refuse and carts it away. Surplus water is drained to the sewer. Large material such as papers and containers have to be broken before being fed into the system. This refuse disposal system has not been extensively used because of its high initial cost and maintenance costs due to careless usage.

Sink waste disposal units: Kitchen waste is fed through the sink waste to a disposal unit in which a grinder powered by a small electric motor reduces the refuse to small particles that are washed down with the waste water from the sink. These units are designed to dispose of such kitchen refuse as food remains which rot and cause disagreeable odours in bins. They are not suited to the disposal of the larger bulky lightweight refuse. Fig. 175 is an illustration of one of these units.

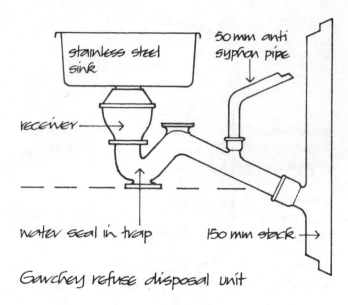

stainless steel sink

50 mm anti syphon pipe

receiver

water seal in trap

150 mm stack →

Gavchey refuse disposal unit

Fig. 174

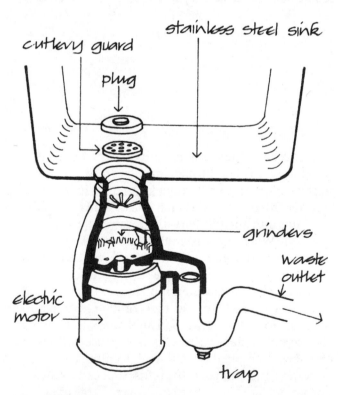

cutlery guard

stainless steel sink

plug

grinders

waste outlet

electric motor

trap

Waste disposal unit

Fig. 175

INDEX